This 3rd edition of *Six steps to RCA* is intended to provide clear guidance to staff tasked with undertaking investigations into adverse events in health and social care (including those categorised by the National Patient Safety Agency as concise or full investigations, serious case reviews, and safeguarding vulnerable adults investigations). It hopes to provide all of its readers with a framework for achieving:

- consistency in their approach to all adverse incident reviews
- a clear and structured methodology
- a strong analytical process
- recommendations that address root causes and have a clear link to the findings of the investigation undertaken
- a participative and proportional process
- a process that is fair and balanced
- a process that ensures that openness prevails with the patient and/or victim, his/her family, the staff involved and any other agency central to the conduct of an effective investigation.

Published by Consequence UK Malvern England

Any queries regarding this publication should be [illegible] the author via: maria@consequenceuk.com

www.consequence.org.uk

ISBN 978-0-9544328-2-9

Acknowledgements

There have been many friends, colleagues and patients, with whom I have worked, and shared my ideas, and without whom I would not have gained the knowledge to make this book possible. I thank them all.

I would like also to thank all of our RCA trainers at Consequence UK Ltd, who bring the richness of their ongoing practice and experience of RCA in the workplace into our training workshops and give so much inspiration and confidence to our trainees.

INDEX

Introduction

Since the first edition of this book, root cause analysis has become central to the modern approach to reviewing significant adverse events in UK healthcare. In England the National Patient Safety Agency (NPSA) launched its RCA e-learning tool kit in 2003 and the Department of Health has shown a consistent determination to have RCA principles incorporated into the investigation of high impact, high profile incidents. The need for a consistent approach to the investigation of adverse incidents is also underlined by the range of standards that health and social care providers are monitored against by organisations such as The Office for Standards in Education, Children's Services and Skills (Ofsted), the National Health Service Litigation Authority (NHSLA) and the Care Quality Commission (CQC).

It is therefore fair to say that the competency with which an organisation manages and learns from adverse incidents has become one of the key markers of success, in relation to risk management and clinical and corporate governance standards.

Overall the standards of investigating NHS incidents and safeguarding incidents have improved since the publication of the first edition of this book in 2002. For the NHS the tools and templates provided by the NPSA and patient safety organisations in the rest of the UK have supported this, and in particular the report writing guidance NPSA has recently produced. For safeguarding incidents, the evaluation of serious case reviews by Ofsted and its commentary on them has resulted in a wholesale improvement in the quality of these investigations.

However, the regular contact the author has with NHS organisations suggests that many continue with an incident investigation approach that lacks clarity and rigour. This applies also to local investigations of safeguarding incidents.

It is the experience of Consequence UK that some of the lack of robustness appears to be caused by the volume of formal investigations required (i.e. investigations culminating in a formal investigation report, be that a concise report following a level 1 investigation or a full report following a level 2 investigation). This is caused in part by the expectation that all incidents scoring a defined grade on a risk assessment matrix will be subject to investigation at level 1 or level 2. It is also caused by the fact that many NHS trusts have not properly clarified the range of investigation approaches that their staff can employ. Too many health organisations continue with a very traditional approach to investigating, with no screening systems in place so that they can make sure that the investigation work conducted is appropriate and proportionate.

There also remain challenges with ensuring that those staff tasked with undertaking level 2 (comprehensive) investigations have the skills and competencies required, and, the time required to deliver a worthwhile investigation. The issue of time continues to be a real thorn in the side of those asked to lead investigations, with many being expected to maintain their day to day responsibilities alongside the investigation process. For complex investigations where serious harm, or death, has occurred this often is just not possible, and those commissioning a comprehensive investigation do have a responsibility to ensure that the appointed investigative lead can free up the necessary time.

The root cause analysis investigation

Before setting out a step by step approach to achieving an effective investigation it is important that there is clarity regarding what we mean by root cause analysis. It has become a term that is used loosely whenever a formal investigation is required, and a term that is employed often without any clarity of understanding by those requesting the conduct of an investigation.

What is root cause analysis?

Root cause analysis (RCA) is a problem solving methodology for discovering the real, or root cause(s) of problems, or difficulties identified via a range of activities, including adverse incident management. It is an approach that is not restricted to the field of incident investigation. RCA tools and techniques such as failure modes and effects analysis, control or barrier analysis, and fault tree analysis are all approaches that can be used to analyse the robustness and reliability of systems and processes in the absence of any problems being apparent, i.e. in the absence of an incident. They are therefore proactive RCA tools. Following an adverse incident, a retrospective analysis is undertaken of the sequence of events leading to it. This analysis will sometimes include the way the incident has been managed. Dependent upon the type of incident and its severity, a structured investigation culminating in a report of the investigation's findings, conclusions and recommendations may be required. An RCA approach may be utilised in the conduct of this. A range of investigation tools such as a timeline, usage of a human factors framework, control analysis, and time person contact grids may help to deliver the RCA approach. However, whichever tools and techniques are utilised, it is essential that they are used within the context of a robust investigation framework.

Such a framework will enable:

- an analytical approach throughout the investigation process;
- the interrogation of what happened, how it happened and why it happened from the perspective of human performance and the performance, or under-performance, of systems and processes designed to support the delivery of safe and effective care;
- the identification of the elements of care/case management and service delivery that were delivered in accordance with the expected standards in place at the time, and those aspects of care/case management and/or service delivery that could and should have been better;
- clarification of any lapses in care/case management or service standards that might be classified as significant and having a quantifiable impact on the incident that subsequently happened (these might be termed significant care/case management or service delivery concerns);
- the identification and differentiation of the range of contributory factors to the significant care/case management or service delivery concerns;
- clarification of those contributory factors that are evidenced as having most impact on each care/case management concern or service delivery concern. These can be called "root causes", or if it is preferred the most significant contributory factors; and
- the generation of recommendations that meet SMART principles and are designed to address the root causes identified.

Health warning

In health and social care, it can be difficult to identify the absolute root cause of care and service delivery problems identified. This is because:

- One's analysis is limited to the information the investigation team were able to collect during the investigation process.
- It is not uncommon for some health and social care incidents to occur "in society" where there are a range of variables which are not under the control of the health or social care organisation.
- It is not uncommon for some health and social care incidents to involve a number of agencies such as probation, the police, education, voluntary sector organisations, housing etc.

These factors do mean that an investigator or investigation team must exercise caution in stating their perspective about the root causes to an identified problem or incident. In the absence of complete data (a common situation in health and social care investigations) an investigator must be honest about the robustness of, and completeness of, evidence upon which he/she is basing root causes. It is disingenuous to state a categorical root cause where the complete picture is not fully understood, and where there is insufficient evidence to back up the promoted root causes.

In such circumstances it is better to say something along the lines of:
"Based upon its analysis of case management concern X, the range of influencing (contributory) factors identified were .... Of these the following are considered to have been most influential:

- ....
- ....
- ...."

Phrasing one's findings in this way keeps the investigation team safe and minimises the risk of incomplete findings being inappropriately exploited.

What does it take to do it well?

The key to a good RCA investigation is the analytical and enquiring mind, coupled with a multitude of what, how and why questions. The successful RCA investigation is the investigation that delivers a detailed analysis of practice, but also presents the context of the system and environment in which the practice was delivered. The successful RCA investigation is also one that pays attention to detail, ensures that it fully explores issues and processes, and does not make assumptions. The investigators will always check out what happened, how something was done and why it was done in a specific way. To achieve the degree of objectivity required to deliver a successful RCA investigation, it is helpful to have at least one person tasked with conducting it who is outside of the service, or services involved in the incident.

Why do it?
Aside from the national performance monitoring drivers, there are two simple reasons why we should commit to undertaking serious incident investigations with rigour. One is that it is not the business of health or social care professionals to cause harm, or contribute to a harmful situation by any human act or omission. The other is that health and social care organisations implement systems and processes they believe will support the delivery of a safe and effective service. If incidents occur because of weakness in those systems and processes, then these need to be identified and put right.

In addition to the above we also owe patients/service users/clients, their families and their carers (where appropriate), and the family of any victim a reasonable explanation of what happened, how it happened and why it happened. As well as being honest with those affected, we must enable them to ask questions, and must put ourselves in the position of being able to answer these questions.

We owe persons harmed (physically, emotionally or psychologically), and the families of any victim the humility of accepting the findings of an investigation that shows we got it wrong, or could have done things better or differently.

We also owe it to ourselves as health and social care professionals to make the necessary improvements to our practice, and the systems and processes underpinning that practice, so that the identified lapses in standards do not happen again.

The following flow chart depicts an incident management process that makes clear local as well as corporate accountability for incident management, investigation of incidents and learning from incidents. The flow chart was originally designed by the author in 1998 for the then Worcester Royal Hospital NHS Trust. It was modified in 2002 and it continues to reflect national expectations for incident management.

INCIDENT REPORTING AND REVIEW PROCESS

INCIDENT OR NEAR MISS OCCURS

IMMEDIATE ACTION

1. Make person(s) /area safe.
2. Obtain medical aid if required.
3. Inform manager on duty ASAP.
4. Complete Incident Form and Risk Assessment of event.

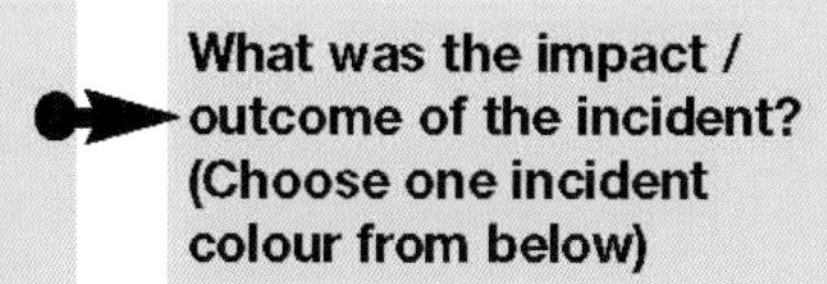

What was the impact / outcome of the incident? (Choose one incident colour from below)

GREEN INCIDENT

No injury or damage caused "Close Call"

YELLOW INCIDENT

Minor injury / damage - i.e no lasting effects, will be resolved in a time period of no-more than 1 month. No major resource implications

It is recommended that for these incidents that the reportee and local manager assess the risk severity of this incident should it recur. If this is considered to be higher than the severity score already assigned consideration should be given to undertaking a more indepth causal investigation or review.

Investigations of Green and Yellow incidents should be undertaken by either the ward manager, departmental manager or clinical team leader. For Yellow events the Directorate Manager (or equivalent) may ask someone outside of the ward to review the event if harm occurred.

For these incidents Managers must be mindful of local systems failures that may need to be addressed and not just address Human Action Failures for this group of incidents.

The local management team are expected to monitor trends associated with this grade of incident and identify where the causal factors are generic to the directorate/area and take appropriate action to address any local system failures identified.

Once the local incident review process is complete the incident form and a copy of any report, or action plan devised, are to be sent to the relevant Risk Manager.

Investigation to be completed within 7 working days

ORANGE INCIDENT

Semi-permanent injury. i.e. will recover but may take some time e.g up to a year or more

The investigation process to be followed is that detailed for Code Red Events. However ownership of the investigation remains with the Directorate Management Team, or equivalent.

All Code Orange event reports, and safety and quality improvement recommendations, will be monitored as part of the Trust's Governance performance monitoring framework.

The Incident form and copy of report are to be sent to the Risk Management Department once completed.

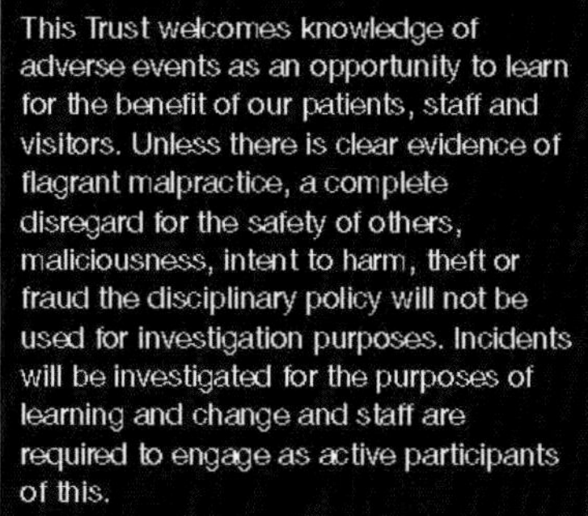

Open and Fair Culture

This Trust welcomes knowledge of adverse events as an opportunity to learn for the benefit of our patients, staff and visitors. Unless there is clear evidence of flagrant malpractice, a complete disregard for the safety of others, maliciousness, intent to harm, theft or fraud the disciplinary policy will not be used for investigation purposes. Incidents will be investigated for the purposes of learning and change and staff are required to engage as active participants of this.

RED INCIDENT

Avoidable death
Major resource implication
Avoidable shortening of life expectancy
Major life long injury e.g. Loss of limb.
Life long loss of service

Report to Senior Manager on Duty
Non-Clinical Risk Manager / Clinical Risk Manager
Executive Office
Patient's Consultant / Lead Clinician

Consider for Full Root Cause Analysis Investigation

Initial system failures identified	No system failures identified.

Full RCA review commissioned. Investigation team appointed, timescales agreed, critical incident meeting arranged with teams involved if appropriate.

Report and recommendations submitted to commissioning committee or Executive Team. Monitoring and review framework agreed.

Recommendations sent to relevant management teams. Decision made to implement recommendations, after consideration of these in the light of existing risk management priorities. Decisions recorded and communicated to Commissioning Team.

Consider need to report to external agencies e.g. SHA / NPSA / HSE / MDA

Investigation to be completed within 45 working days

Reporting of Injuries, Diseases and Dangerous Occurrences Regulations 1995 (RIDDOR)
Report all RIDDOR reportable events to Health & Safety Advisor on ext 9102 or e-mail on h.safety@consequence.org.uk

Report all Medical Device Events to Health & Safety Advisor on ext 9102 or Medical Equiptment co-ordinator on ext 1302 or email on h.safety@consequence.org.uk or med.equip@consequence.org.uk

Report all staff sickness precipitated by an accident at work to Occupational Health on ext 8543

RIDDOR reportable events are:
Any fracture (not fingers or toes) I Amputations I Dislocation of Joint
Loss of sight I Chemical, hot burn to eye I Any electric shock requiring resuscitation I Hypothermia, or heat induced illness ILoss of consciousness - asphyxia I Acute illness caused by biological substance

If in doubt contact the H&S advisor on ext 9102 or e-mail on h.safety@consequence.org.uk

An open and fair culture

To achieve the effective investigation of adverse incidents, staff must feel safe to report incidents and safety issues. They must also be willing to share with investigators their involvement with the patient or service involved in an incident. To feel safe staff need to trust that the information they share will be treated with respect and acted upon appropriately, for the overall improvement of the safety and quality of health and social care services provided to patients/clients/service users. And also the improvement in the working environment for staff, visitors and contractors where this is indicated as necessary.

Staff do not, and should not, need any guarantee of a "blame free" environment. What they can, and should, expect is that all the information is objectively analysed by persons appropriately knowledgeable and competent to do so. Staff should also expect that the investigator/investigation team will look at what happened in the full knowledge of all relevant material information, and will balance the varying contribution of system lapses and human contribution (if indeed there were any slips in performance) in formulating the findings, conclusions and recommendations of the investigation.

Employees of an organisation should not feel that they are at risk of being a scapegoat when a serious incident occurs. Similarly employees should expect to step up to their professional accountabilities and responsibilities and not expect "the system" to be the "fall guy". It is important to the concept of natural justice that professional staff accept and learn from any contribution they may have made to the sequence of events leading to a subsequent serious incident.

To achieve a just culture within the incident investigation process, it must be

- fair and equitable;
- focused on learning and change, and not on personalities;
- focused on identifying contributory factors and root causes; and
- non-punitive where possible.

This should mean that:

- Each organisation will have a clearly defined culpability framework, so that decisions to look specifically at individual practitioners' professional performance are made within a consistently applied decision matrix. The NPSA's *Incident decision tree* provides such a framework (http://www.nrls.npsa.nhs.uk/resources/?EntryId45=59900).
- The disciplinary process is only to be used where it is clear that the actions of those involved included:
  - ✓ an intention to harm;
  - ✓ a criminal act;
  - ✓ acts that put the safety of patients, visitors, contractors or colleagues at risk, and that this risk was clearly predictably by virtue of the individual's actions;
  - ✓ a flagrant disregard for the well being and safety of others; and
  - ✓ repeated safety breaches over time with no improvement in performance in spite of appropriate supervision, training and support.

All organisations should make clear the distinction between their incident management and disciplinary policies, and ensure that there are no contradictions contained within them. For example, you do not want a disciplinary policy with a "broad brush" approach in respect of policy violations. Ideally a disciplinary policy will reflect the need for a balanced analysis of poor performance, and encourage those conducting professional performance investigations to consider whether a policy violation constituted an exceptional or circumstantial violation (The NPSA has termed this a "reasoned" violation), or a frequently recurring violation (The NPSA has termed this a "routine" violation) Reference, NPSA (2010) Glossary – root cause analysis, www.nrls.npsa.nhs.uk/resources/?entryid45=75602.

Essentially as far as the investigation is concerned, although the impetus for a disciplinary investigation is different to that of a learning investigation, the standards of investigation should be just as robust, if not more so, including appropriate consideration of system influences on an individual's practice.

Being open

When things go wrong in health or social care it is very important that the involved organisations have a culture of openness and honesty with the patient, the client, the victim, families and carers. Historically there has been a shield of secrecy around unexpected adverse outcomes of care management or case management. This has never been helpful. The adversely affected family naturally believes that the involved organisation is "covering up" and for the health and social care professionals, a lack of openness is akin to dishonesty which does not sit well with professional codes of conduct.

When there is an unexpected adverse poor outcome for a patient/child/client/service user, there must be openness with the individual affected and their immediate family and/or carer wherever possible. Where the harmed person is a victim of a violent act, such as the victim of a mental health homicide, the duties of the organisation responsible for the mental health patient are the same as if the victim was one of their patients. Victims' families also have a right to know what happened and how.

All have a right to know:

- what happened;
- how it happened;
- why it happened;
- what the organisation is doing to remedy any harm caused;
- what the organisation is going to do to improve its systems and processes so that there is less chance of another person experiencing the same, or similar adverse outcome (where this has been shown to have been preventable) with more appropriate care/treatment/surveillance including actions by the staff involved; and
- what the organisation is going to do to address weaknesses in its systems that have been identified during the investigation process, but which did not impact on the subsequent poor outcome that occurred.

The former Association of Victims of Medical Accidents (AVMA), now renamed Action against Medical Accidents (AvMA)[1] says:

"A 'medical accident' is where avoidable harm has been caused as a result of treatment or failure to treat appropriately. AvMA believes that whatever the cause of a medical accident, the people affected deserve explanations, support, and where appropriate, compensation. Furthermore, we all deserve to know that the necessary steps will be taken to prevent similar accidents being repeated."

The NPSA's *Being open* guidance[2], relaunched in November 2009, says:

"Being open involves:

- acknowledging, apologising and explaining when things go wrong;
- conducting a thorough investigation into the incident and reassuring patients, their families and carers that lessons learned will help prevent the incident recurring; and
- providing support for those involved to cope with the physical and psychological consequences of what happened.

It is important to remember that saying sorry is not an admission of liability and is the right thing to do.

The principles

The following set of principles has been developed to help healthcare organisations create and embed a culture of being open:

- acknowledgement;
- truthfulness, timeliness and clarity of communication;
- apology;
- recognising patient and carer expectations; and
- professional support."

These principles also apply to social care incidents.

[1] http://www.avma.org.uk/

[2] NPSA (2009) *Being open* alert and guidance. http://www.nrls.npsa.nhs.uk/resources/?entryid45=65077

How to be open

There are a number of obstacles for health and social care staff in achieving a true culture of openness with patients/clients/service users, and families/carers/victims when things seem to have gone wrong. These are:

- Staff are trying to deal with their own anxieties about whether or not something they did or did not do contributed to what has happened.
- Staff are worried about "getting into trouble".
- Staff don't know how to tell the patient/client/family.
- Staff don't know how to make contact with the victim's family in the case of a mental health homicide.
- Staff don't know how to broach the subject of the internal investigation with the victim's family following a mental health homicide.

All of these are understandable. Therefore, in each organisation there should be staff of appropriate seniority who are properly trained in speaking to patients/clients/families when serious adverse incidents occur. These staff should have the competencies to:

- meet with the care team and obtain a rounded understanding of the circumstances of what has happened;
- meet with the family accompanied by the clinical team leader or case manager responsible, and make an apology for what has happened: "I/we am/are very sorry that you are having this experience. We do not know how this happened but we are going to investigate your (child's/partner's/father's/mother's etc) care/case management and do our best to find out what happened, how it happened and why it happened.";
- find out what the family/patient/client wants. Are there questions that they would like answers to? How involved do they want to be? And listen.

Such an individual should also be tasked with the responsibility of maintaining regular contact with the family during the investigation process so that they are not left wondering what is happening.

In some cases the nominated investigation lead may have the competencies noted above, however that is not always the case and competency should not be assumed.

At the end of the investigation process, families should be offered the opportunity to meet with the same member of staff with whom they originally had contact, with or without relevant senior managers and clinicians. The purpose of such a meeting would be to take the family (and patient/client/service user) through the findings of the investigation, its overall conclusions and recommendations.

It is not acceptable simply to send a family a copy of the investigation report. They must be supported through their initial reading of this. Doing this presents a valuable opportunity to explain in plain English what has happened and to enable the service user/patient/client/family to ask questions of clarification. It is also an opportunity for them to highlight to the organisation whether their original questions have been answered or not and whether or not they are satisfied with the investigation conducted.

Readers interested in knowing more about being open should read the NPSA's *Being open* alert and guidance 2009.

http://www.nrls.npsa.nhs.uk/resources/?entryid45=65077

A brief overview of human error from an investigator's perspective

All staff leading serious incident investigations and safeguarding serious case reviews should have at least a basic understanding of human error and accident causation theory. This is essential to enable investigators to conduct an investigation that embraces the principles of root cause analysis i.e. the systems focused investigation. It is also essential in order to achieve balance in the analysis of any significant care or service delivery concerns identified during the investigation process. It is the balanced consideration of the human and system contribution to identified lapses in performance that enables an open and fair culture to prevail. Investigators also need to understand the basics of human error and accident causation theory to differentiate between the "root" and "proximal" causes to identified practice and system lapses.

Most texts on the subject of accident causation refer to James Reason's eminent and widely respected work in this field, and in particular, the "Swiss cheese" model[3]. However, from the investigator's perspective, the author has found the presentation of the Wheel of Misfortune[4], developed by David O'Hare in 2000, to be most helpful. It is this model that is presented here.

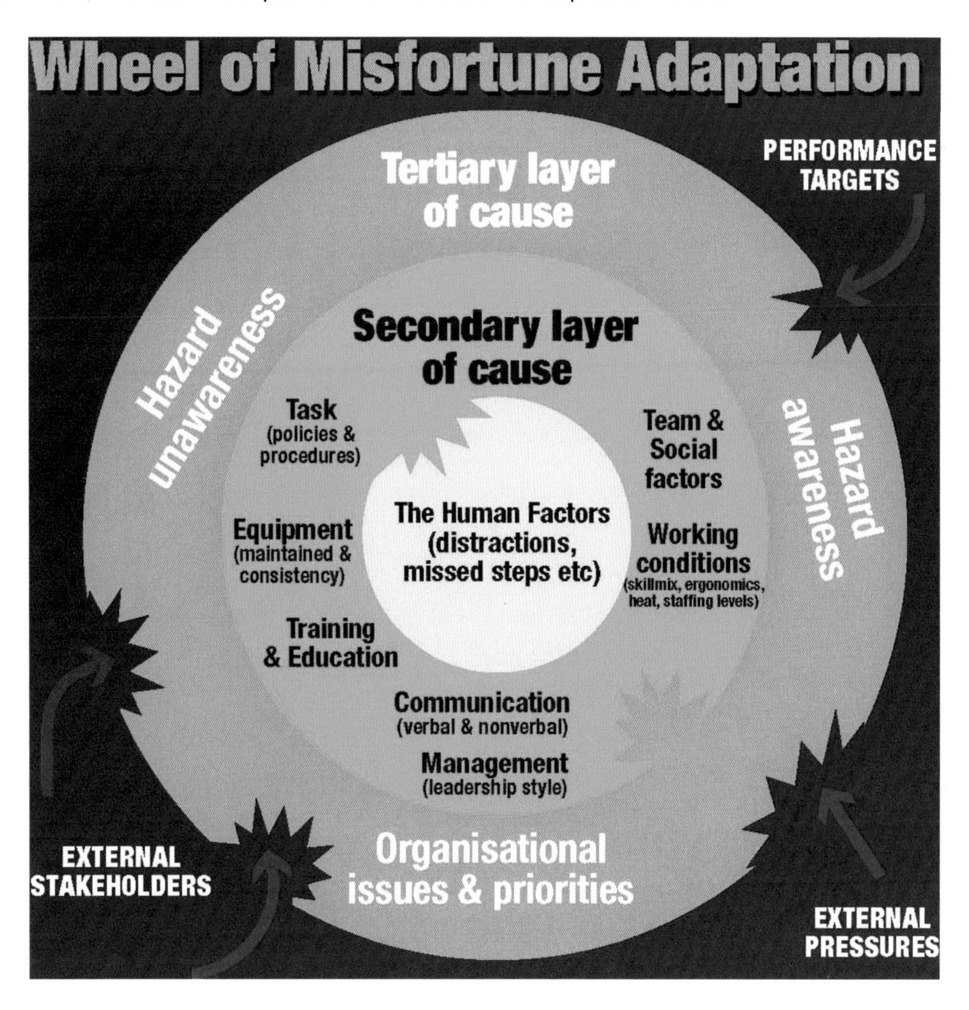

The Wheel of Misfortune accurately depicts the investigator's world. Practitioners are often closest to the incident that has occurred and they are surrounded by systems and processes intended to enable them to deliver their responsibilities well. The investigator's role is to gain a firm understanding of both, as far as reasonably can be achieved within the boundaries of the investigation, and the agreed terms of reference.

---

[3] The Swiss Cheese model forms an integral component of our understanding of human error and accident causation theory and is widely referred to in texts and in conferences. The reader may wish to access *Human error* by James Reason, published by Cambridge Press in 1990, ISBN 0-52131419-4 to read in more detail Prof. Reason's theories regarding human error.

[4] David O'Hare (2000) "The 'Wheel of Misfortune': a taxonomic approach to human factors in accident investigation and analysis in aviation and other complex systems", *Ergonomics*, vol 43, no 12, pp2001-2019.

Why do we make mistakes?

The list is endless, and includes the following:

- lapses in concentration;
- distraction errors as a result of activities such as mentally multitasking or interfering with someone else's task;
- distraction errors because we have stressors in our home life that are dominating our thoughts;
- misunderstanding of what was expected of us;
- misinterpretation of data/information;
- being unfamiliar with a task and missing out a crucial step in the process;
- being complacent due to over-familiarity;
- being inexperienced and devising a well thought out but wrong plan; and
- being busy and missing out steps in safety procedures.

This fallibility can lead to critical actions and inactions by staff that sometimes have a devastating impact on a client's, patient's, or service user's case or care management.

Some examples of this are:

"The junior doctor was busy and over stretched. He had been told to prescribe antibiotics for Mrs A. He did so but without reading her notes or speaking with her. He assumed that because the instruction had come from a more senior doctor that a penicillin based antibiotic, as was usually prescribed, was what was required in this case. Unfortunately Mrs A had a life-threatening allergy to penicillin. She was subsequently administered the IV antibiotic preparation prescribed, to which she reacted severely. Mrs A lost her life as a result of this mistake."

"The surgical team was in the process of completing a procedure. It was identified that it was one swab down. The team prided itself on not leaving swabs in patients; in fact the team's belief was that it never left swabs in patients. Consequently the operation was completed in knowledge that there was a swab missing "because it couldn't be in the patient". At the end of the procedure, after the patient had been moved to recovery, the swab remained missing. The patient had to be taken back to theatre the following day for removal of the swab."

"Mrs A had end stage heart failure. She also had a high anxiety state that staff on the medical ward found difficult to manage. Because Mrs A was considered fit for discharge home for a long weekend, but did not feel able to go because of her anxiety levels, the medical team asked the mental health team if she could be transferred to their service for the management of her anxiety. Mrs A was supportive of this. A good handover occurred between the two teams. The following day it was quiet on the mental health ward and the nurse administering the medicines changed her normal routine, taking the medicines to the patients rather than the patients attending at the treatment room. A drug error occurred. Mrs A was given 160mg of slow release propanolol. The nurse reported her error and asked for the on call medic to attend. However neither the nurse nor the senior house officer recognised the significance of the error. This was not realised until Mrs A was found collapsed on the floor by her bed. By this time, although the resuscitation team were called, it was too late to save the life of Mrs A."

"Miss B had a bipolar disorder and had reduced as far as possible her medication regime. Over the Christmas period she became unwell and self presented at A&E. She was so unwell the psychiatric liaison team had difficulty in assessing her. Appropriately, the crisis resolution and home treatment team were asked to attend to conduct an assessment to determine whether or not home treatment would be an option for Miss B or whether hospital treatment was required. The crisis resolution and home treatment team attended a few hours later by which time Miss B had settled. She was able to converse freely with the crisis team. She asked them if she would be able to be treated at home as she had been successfully treated at home before. In fact the mental health professionals had both visited her at home before. They conducted their assessment and concluded that home treatment was an appropriate way forward for Miss B, and they arranged for further mental health assessment to take place the following morning with the crisis resolution consultant psychiatrist. In determining that Miss B was suitable for home treatment the mental health professionals had assumed that she had someone at home to support her. They also assumed that because she had taken a larger than normal dose of her normal medication they could not give her further antipsychotic medication. Their recollection from their previous contact with her was that she had someone at home with her, when in fact she did not. Furthermore it was the established custom and practice of the team not to utilise the support and advice of the duty psychiatric team out of hours. When Miss B became very unwell overnight there was no-one to call for help and Miss B was involved in a serious incident resulting in the loss of life of two members of the public."

All of the above scenarios reveal a range of human errors that made a contribution to enabling the incidents that subsequently occurred. In "investigation speak" these errors would be articulated as case or care management concerns.

In contrast Service delivery concerns would be something like:

"There was no effective training and competency assessment process to ensure that midwives and medical staff working on the labour ward could accurately interpret cardiotocograph readings (i.e. the baby's heart trace)."

"The operational policy for the crisis team had been ineffectual for a period of six years. This had not been identified by the management team for this service and meant that basic standards of practice were not being delivered."

"The trust has no medicines safety programme for nursing and medical staff."

"The trust had been aware for some three years of the deficiencies in practice relating to (mental health) nursing observations. No action plan had been agreed to remedy the problem."

"There is no agreed protocol for how home agency A and agency B should communicate with each other or where such communication should be recorded. "

"Care home A has not determined the core skills and competencies required of its qualified and support staff, consequently the annual programme of education does not deliver the necessary skills and competencies to deliver person-centred care to the vulnerable adults in its care."

Note: None of the scenarios detailed above are straightforward. All are based on real life events and all have a range of complexities not immediately obvious from the scenarios presented. The RCA or systems based investigation would need to unpack the scenarios and properly understand the sequencing of events, what was in the minds of the professionals involved, what the normal model of work was and the systems and processes in place to guide practitioners in their actions and decision making. It is with this process that tools such as the Wheel of Misfortune can aid the thinking of the investigator.

The Wheel of Misfortune helps us understand that at work we are part of a wider system. This system consists of four interconnecting layers:

- The centre of the wheel which represents the human behaviour.
- The middle layer, which represents all of the systems, process and controls that have been designed to support and enable employees and contractors to do their job safely and to the best of their ability. Any weaknesses identified in these systems will usually have been present for some time and can be termed latent in their nature, though this is not always the case. The National Patient Safety Agency describes weaknesses identified in this layer as "service delivery problems" (SDPs). SDPs may be contributory to care/case management concerns or they may be a 'root cause' of the care/case management concern.
- The tertiary layer represents:
  - organisational decision making;
  - the vision and values of the organisation;
  - the organisation's safety culture;
  - the organisation's degree of "hazard awareness" or "unawareness".
- The outer layer or "atmosphere" in which the organisation sits. This embraces the external influences to the organisation. It is this layer over which an organisation usually has no control.

Weakness identified across the middle, tertiary and outer layers can often have a delayed impact on the delivery of frontline care and are therefore often grouped under the heading of latent failures. However it is possible for decisions and failures, within these layers, to have a direct impact in the genesis of an incident.
An investigator should explore at least the central and inner circle of the wheel to gain a grounded appreciation of how and why things have happened. Where possible, and where appropriate, an understanding of the tertiary layer can be helpful. This layer, although primarily targeting organisational culture, can be applied to service wide management culture and local team culture.

For investigations that do not meet the criteria for a public inquiry, the tertiary and outer layers of the Wheel of Misfortune can be the most challenging to explore. Often they will not be explored because it is not proportionate to the incident to do so.

Key points

1) When investigating local incidents (including complaints) it can be helpful to segregate the outer layer of the Wheel of Misfortune into local team management, service wide management, and organisation wide management. Doing this enables issues such as management decision making, vision and values to be explored on an appropriate and proportional basis.

2) Investigators and organisations need to be mindful that assigning local managers to investigate significant incidents on "their patch" may create barriers to achieving an open and thorough review of the systems and processes, especially if the investigator had a responsibility for the functioning of these.

3) Where to find more information.
If you want to expand your knowledge of error causation a good starting point is to access the NPSA's e-learning RCA tool kit. This can be accessed via www.nrls.npsa.nhs.uk/resources/?entryid45=59901, or by conducting an internet search using the search terms 'NPSA RCA tool kit'.

Case study 1

This case study aims to highlight the importance of having a rounded understanding of the antecedents to an incident, as well as the incident itself.

In 2001 the author worked as the associate director of governance in a mental health trust. An incident was reported where an inpatient had attempted suicide by hanging. This resulted in permanent brain injury for the service user. An investigation was undertaken following incident notification. There were many issues that arose from this. These were:

- Estates management. The wardrobe doors were fixed with four double hinges to prevent the doors from falling off.
- The custom and practice amongst ward staff in the mornings of going into the nursing office immediately after the handover between the night and the day staff, to do the allocations for the day.
- The system for how new equipment such as telephones was made ready for use on the wards.
- The culture of nursing observation practice.
- Staff knowledge of the emergency contact number to elicit a fast response from the medical team.
- Nursing staff members' perceptions of the medical staff.

The lapses in nursing observation practice were discussed at the then clinical improvement committee. A "no action" decision was made, and it was recommended that nursing staff should be more diligent at following the nursing observation policy instructions. Key personnel present considered that the policy document met with existing national standards at the time. It was not considered important to look further at the underlying cultural issues and tensions between nursing and medical staff. There were more pressing clinical quality and safety issues to be addressed.

Approximately six months after this incident an inpatient suicide occurred in a different inpatient area, and in a completely different part of the county. Furthermore the circumstances of the second incident were very different from the first. However, there was a question over staff adherence to the nursing observation policy at an early stage of the investigation process. A decision was made that this element of nursing practice should be explored under the disciplinary policy. This caused considerable strength of feeling among a number of nurse managers. In the event no disciplinary investigation was conducted. The reason for this was the previous decision of the clinical improvement committee not to undertake a root and branch review of the approach to nursing observations within general adult services, or the culture of practice. A "weak" solution to the previous concerns had been implemented, i.e. telling staff to follow the policy. Essentially the clinical improvement committee had accepted that there may be some deficiencies in the policy document and deficiencies in practice, but that that these were not significant enough at the time to warrant further action. Because the organisation was "hazard aware" it was not appropriate to commence the new investigation from a disciplinary perspective. It needed to be a holistic, systems focused approach. To have taken the person focused approach would have unreasonably scapegoated the nursing staff.

Determining the right approach to the investigation of the second incident raised an important issue for managers within the trust. This issue was – how does one know if, following a previous incident, the service or organisation has decided to "carry" a risk and not address possible policy deficiencies or unhealthy cultural issues? In trying to ensure consistency of approach and a just culture managers felt it was important that they could easily find out this information.

The author suspects that the level of transparency managers were looking for in 2001 continues to remain elusive. However, use of the NPSA's *Incident decision tree* should mean that a decision to progress an investigation via the disciplinary process is based on good quality information and not solely on the opinion of an individual or group.

The investigation process

Step one:

Commissioning an investigation, and framing and clarifying its scope

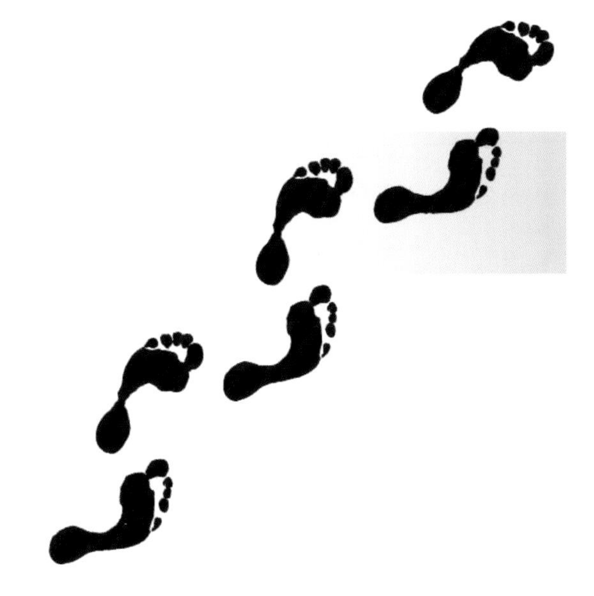

1.1 Overview

Whenever an incident occurs that requires a structured or comprehensive investigation culminating in an formal investigation report, there should be a clearly defined process for how these investigations are instructed. It is not acceptable for staff to merely receive an email advising them of an incident and asking them to investigate!

The key considerations before the green light is given to the investigation process are:

- What approach needs to be taken to the investigation?
- How can a proportional approach be achieved?
- What are the terms of reference going to be?
- Who is the right person to lead the investigation process and what specialist input is required?
- What is the existing workload for the identified investigation lead and does this fit with the demands of this investigation?
- Which managers and lead clinicians need to be advised that a serious incident investigation is to occur so that they can ensure that all relevant staff are available when required to provide information to the investigation team?
- What, if any, administrative support is available?

1.2 What to investigate?

The answer to this question is largely provided within the national risk management standards and also in the NPSA's document *Three levels of RCA investigation – guidance*[5]. At this time all NHS organisations should have a risk assessment process that enables them to accurately identify those incidents that require investigations (a risk assessment process is detailed in Appendix A.18 of this book).

However what is not currently provided is clear guidance on what constitutes a valid investigation, or what constitutes a valid process for determining whether or not an investigation is required for an incident attracting a "code red" score using a risk assessment matrix. Not all code red incidents require an investigation. Some code red incidents are "act of God" incidents such as a stillbirth, others occur outside the control of the health and social care services, such as community suicide, and harm to vulnerable children or adults. In all cases, one would want to conduct some level of incident analysis to ensure that there were no apparent lapses on the part of the health or social care provided that could have made a difference. However this analysis does not necessarily require an investigation in the form commonly applied (i.e. a full traditional style investigation).

---

[5] Reference: `www.nrls.npsa.nhs.uk/resources/?entryid45=75355'

The bullet points below set out a range of options that might reasonably constitute an "investigation". The key is the level of independence of the staff performing the incident and/or case notes analysis at the initial screening of the incident.

The range of investigative approaches are:

- Independent[6] clinical case notes review by one or two suitably experienced professionals skilled in the area of work in which the incident occurred. This enables a view to be taken early on regarding the appropriateness and reasonableness of the care or case management. The output from this first level review can enable a service or organisation to determine what, if anything, requires further investigation.
- Reflective round-the-table discussion with the team involved in the antecedents to the incident and the post incident management. Ideally such a meeting would be facilitated by someone not in the team and involve an independent specialist in the field.
- The traditional approach, i.e. case notes analysis followed up by individual and/or group interviews with staff, undertaken by a specifically appointed investigation team of two to three persons from outside the team/service.
- Starting the process with a "systems walk through" to create a control map and a map of how the process/procedure should have occurred. This should be undertaken by the appointed investigation lead who has little or no knowledge of the process under investigation supported by someone who knows the system/process very well. Following this, a decision can be made about the subsequent scope of any further investigation required.
- A blended approach that is a hybrid of the above.

For health and social care providers to be able to deliver the volume of investigations that can be required, it is important that there is no blind adherence to national guidelines. All this achieves is a high volume of cases to be investigated, with insufficient attention being afforded to those cases that deserve a careful and considered analysis. Health and social care organisations must ensure that they implement an intelligent approach to the subsequent screening of those incidents/occurrences attracting a code red, or high risk, rating so that proportionality in approach is achieved and that the right investigation approach is agreed on early in the process.

1.3 Who should commission an investigation?

Because this book is concerned with an organisation's approach to incident investigation, the following list identifies the types of groups, persons, and committees that are ideally placed to commission an incident investigation. Examples of these are:

- executive/senior management team;
- corporate risk management committee or governance committee;
- heads of service and directorate/divisional managers;
- governance/safety managers;
- medical director, nursing director, head of social care etc.

1.4 The role of those commissioning an investigation

Whether or not a root cause analysis investigation is required there are some core responsibilities held by persons, or groups, asking for and commissioning an investigation following a serious incident. These responsibilities include:

- Ensuring that the investigation team has the full support and authorisation of the investigation's commissioners to conduct the investigation, and that this has been made explicit to all service managers whose staff are likely to be involved.
- That the terms of reference for the investigation are clearly defined and relevant (see the example on the following page).
- That appropriately skilled and competent persons are tasked with undertaking the investigation.
- That a project plan is agreed with the appointed investigation team, which sets out the stages of the investigation and the anticipated time frames for each stage.
- That dates for briefings on progress are agreed at the start of the process.
- That reasonable administrative support is secured to ensure maximum efficiencies for the investigation team.

---

[6] Independent means independent of the team and preferably the service, or division, in which the incident occurred. Independence from the team should be achievable. It may not always be possible to identify suitable professionals from outside a service or division.

It must be made clear to the investigation team that they are accountable for:

- The quality of the investigation.
- The manner in which they carry out their investigation.
- Updating the commissioning group on the progress of the investigation, including any difficult areas.
- Communicating the findings and recommendations of the investigation to key interviewees/witnesses, so that they can provide feedback on this or ask for the evidence base if this is not clear and transparent. Consideration must be given to providing all key interviewees with a copy of the draft investigation report to comment upon before its content is finalised.
- Providing a comprehensive structured and clear investigation report that sets out the investigation team's findings, conclusions and recommendations.

Example terms of reference

1. To establish a clear and complete chronology of what happened between *date X and date Y.*
2. To examine:
   - The appropriateness of the service user's/patient's/client's initial care/case management plan, and the robustness of the initial history/information recorded.
   - The appropriateness of any:
     - medical management plan;
     - care plan; and
     - risk assessments and risk management plans.
   - The communications between the regular care/case management team and with other involved teams and/or agencies including those in the voluntary/tertiary sectors.
   - The pattern of contact between the care/case management team and the service user/patient/client, and where these contacts were successful or unsuccessful.
3. Where significant concerns are identified in relation to the key elements identified at point 2, the contributory factors for any serious lapse in care/case management or service weakness must be identified, and where possible the most significant influencing factors (i.e. root causes) to these lapses.
4. To make recommendations to address the most significant influencing factors (root causes) identified.
5. To write an investigation report with integral executive summary that sets out clearly the investigation team's findings, recommendations and conclusions.

In delivering the above it is expected that the investigation team will appropriately review and reference:

- relevant local and national policies;
- supervision of staff;
- team dynamics;
- across agency/service relationship issues;
- team leadership;
- environmental issues where appropriate; and
- workplace and task design issues where appropriate. (Note this includes the appropriateness of the guidance included in local and national policies, their ease of use, and their availability).

It is also assumed that the investigation team will:

- Embrace the best practice principles in *Being open* and communicate effectively with the affected service user/carer/client and his or her family and/or carers.
- Consider the principles of the National Patient Safety Agency's *Incident decision tree* and in particular the substitution test, where the investigation team is of the opinion that the involved team should have managed the situation with the client/patient/service user differently.
- Adhere to national guidance on the conduct of a serious case review as outlined in chapter 8 of Working Together to Safeguard Children

1.5 The investigation team

It is good practice for a serious incident investigation to be undertaken by more than one person. This helps guard against the superimposition of an individual's perspective on the investigation outcome and also guards against avenues of inquiry not being explored because of an investigator's intimate knowledge, or experience, of the area under investigation, or conversely his/her lack of knowledge of the area.

It is suggested that a balanced investigation team comprises:

- A lead investigator (from outside of the service involved in the incident).
- At least one, preferably two professionals with the right balance of experience and expertise within the service(s) involved, but not from the team or teams involved in the care or service delivery.

There will be times when workload demands that a sole investigator is appointed. In such circumstances the commissioner(s) of the investigation must be aware of the risks they are taking with the overall robustness of the investigation when doing so. In such circumstances the appointed investigator can ensure that he/she secures some additional independence and objectivity into key stages of the process. For example, when initially reviewing the available written evidence, and when analysing the information gathered during the investigation process.

Ideally organisations should have a register of staff who are competent to undertake an investigation into serious incidents. Persons on such a register should have attended an investigation workshop delivered by a competent provider or individual. Persons on the register should also be expected to lead a minimum of two serious incident investigations per year. Competency in this field, as in many fields, is obtained by practice and reflection, i.e. by time served experience.

Where possible, when persons are entered onto an organisation's register of investigators they should be buddied with a more experienced investigator until they are confident and competent to lead investigations independently.

1.6 Scoping an investigation

This can be challenging. It may not be possible to determine the absolute scope of an investigation until there has been an initial case notes analysis and perhaps some initial discussions with key staff so that the sequence of events and potential issues for exploration can be established. Then the investigation team, and therefore the commissioners, will have a clearer idea of:

- what aspects of the case management appear to have been delivered to an acceptable standard; and
- what aspects of the case management there are concerns about.

It is at this point that realistic terms of reference may need to be agreed, or those previously provided revisited.

Where an incident have occurred and there is no antecedent path leading to it for example a diagnostic error in a laboratory, the scope of the investigation will need to include the creation of a full system map before the investigators can consider establishing what happened in the incident scenario. Sensible questions about what happened and why will most appropriately be generated once the investigation team has an understanding of how the process should work without error.

Note: For specialist mental health care providers it is established practice for the local manager of the team whose patient has been involved in a serious incident to conduct a "72 hour review". This means that the local manager pulls together the chronology of what has happened including sufficient antecedents for him or her to form an early opinion as to the adequacy of the care and treatment provided to the service user. These perspectives can be useful in enabling the commissioners of any subsequent investigation to identify an appropriate terms of reference. At the time of writing, many mental health trusts are not capitalising on this established process to ensure proportionality in subsequently undertaken comprehensive investigations.

Note 2: When it is known that a serious case review is being considered each involved organisation is required to conduct an individual management review (IMR). The completeness and robustness of the IMR can and should impact on the subsequent scope of the serious case review. The IMR should therefore meet the standards expected of all comprehensive investigations.

The investigation process

Step two:

Collecting, Sorting and Mapping Information

2.0 Introduction

Step Two represents the start of the active phase of the investigation process. It is where the investigation team "gets going".

The active phases of all investigations require a number of core activities. These are:

- The collection and analysis of readily accessible information.
- The gathering of further information to enable the investigation team to conduct a comprehensive assessment of the care and management provided to the patient/client/child/family.
- The structured analysis of information gathered during the investigation to achieve clarity regarding what was done well and what could, or should, have been done better. The analysis of the information should also leave the investigation team with a clear understanding of the contributory factors to each aspect of care/case management that could/should have been done better. From the often broad range of contributory factors those of greatest significance will generally emerge.
- The formulation of recommendations designed to address the contributory factors of greatest significance.
- The writing and presentation of the investigation report.

The activities around which Step Two focus are:

- the identification of what information to collect;
- the collection of the information;
- the analysis of the information using methodologies such as timelining and process mapping; and
- further information gathering to address the gaps in the investigation team's knowledge and understanding.

2.1 Activities in the immediate aftermath of the incident that make Step Two easier

It is essential that all material facts surrounding the incident, its antecedents and its consequences, are collected as soon as possible after the incident. Formal investigations can be conducted weeks, months and sometimes years after an incident has occurred. Consequently the initial actions of local managers, in the initial collection of, and retention of information are important.
In the immediate aftermath of a serious incident, local managers/team leaders should:

- Ensure that all clinical/case management records are gathered together as soon as possible and stored securely. A log of all records secured should be made and appended to the relevant record on the organisation's risk management database. Where records are likely to be required by the coroner's office and/or police, where possible a good quality photocopy should be made of all records before the original records are released. The organisation's risk manager and/or records manager should be able to provide advice about this. The information manager and/or Caldicott guardian for the organisation may also be able to advise.
- Ensure that the case records/clinical records made by staff are as complete as possible. This means that the local manager must review these within 72 hours of the incident and where records are found to be lacking in completeness, staff can be invited to make a retrospective record, setting out clearly any contact they had with the patient/client/child/family etc, actions taken, communications with other colleagues, agencies etc. It is essential that the staff member states clearly that the record has been made in retrospect and why complete records were not made at the time. All retrospective records must be clearly dated, the staff member should print their name, and then sign their records.
- Encourage each involved member of staff to make a personal record of their contacts with the patient/client/child etc during:
  - the period of time leading to the incident (i.e. antecedents);
  - the incident itself; and
  - the post-incident management if they were involved in this.

  This document should not be viewed as a statement as it is unlikely to be formulated as such. However it should be as complete as possible, including the staff member's rationale for actions and non-actions, communications with other colleagues and agencies etc. In short it should contain a depth and breadth of information that will generally not be found in any clinical or case management record. All staff must be advised that this record should be stored safely, so that they can refer to it at a later date should a formal internal and/or independent investigation be commissioned. Ideally the staff member will provide a copy of their personal account to their line manager for safe keeping. NB: When staff make their personal statements these should always be written in the first person, i.e. "I did", "I said", "I saw". It is acceptable to say "Mr/Ms X asked me to ... and I carried out this instruction". However, staff must be advised not to give any opinion about the actions of other colleagues in this document.
- Where it is the policy of the employing organisation to take "statements" from staff then these must be collected properly. This means that staff must be provided with guidance on how to write a statement, and someone with the right competencies to review and comment on this for the staff member is available to do so. (An organisation's risk manager or legal services manager would be the type of person who should be able to do this).
- Ensure that any equipment involved is taken out of service and managed in line with the organisation's equipment management policies and also the Medicines and Healthcare products Regulation Agency (MHRA) guidelines. If photographs need to be taken of the equipment in situ then wherever possible this should occur. The health and safety manager/risk manager should be able to provide the necessary support and equipment for this.

> In the aftermath of an incident memory loss will occur. However if the incident was particularly memorable or traumatic, memory loss is much less affected by the passage of time. If staff are given the right time and space to remember what happened, memory recall can be very good. However many workplace incidents are not all that memorable to the individuals who may have had contact with the patient, child, client etc. This is why encouraging staff to make a record of everything they can remember as soon as possible after an incident is important.

2.2 Early activities required of the appointed investigator or investigation team in serious incident investigations

If you have been asked to undertake a serious incident investigation, you have a number of tasks to complete before considering which staff you may want to interview and what you may want to explore with them.

In brief these activities are:

- Conducting a thorough analysis of any available written information that may enable the construction of a detailed chronology of events.
- Identifying what questions need to be asked about the case/care management and also of the systems and processes that should have been supporting the effective delivery of the care/case management.
- Identifying which people you need to interview to answer the identified questions. Note, this range of persons may be more extensive than those directly involved in the process, patient care pathway or case management.

In determining what information to collect you must consider the lead up to, as well as the incident itself. Sometimes the "start point" for the investigation may be crystal clear, on other occasions it may not be. For some complex incidents it is only by starting with the incident and working backwards through time that the relevant period to be included in the investigation can be identified. On other occasions, especially in relation to acute inpatient episodes, and other inpatient scenarios, it may be appropriate to review the complete patient journey from admission to incident NB**:** There is no one approach that suits all investigations. The approach taken must be decided on an incident by incident basis and by means of consensus amongst the investigation team, plus/minus the commissioners of the investigation.

2.2.1 The Five P's

To ensure that information is collected from all available sources, both in terms of the specific actions that led to the event, and the factors underlying it, the investigators will find it helpful to consider the availability of information from a range of sources. These will usually constitute:

- the **P**eople involved or who were witnesses;
- the **P**lace or environment in which the incident took place;
- the **P**arts, equipment or moving parts, objects involved in the incident;
- the **P**aperwork related to the incident (policies, procedures, local and national guidelines, case records, supervision records, training records etc); and
- the existing **P**aradigms, i.e. the widely held beliefs about the normal working processes, team relationships, and adequacy of leadership in the work place.

This list has been referred to as the Five Ps.

1. From PERSONS involved in the incident

It is not uncommon for the following information to be available to the investigation team prior to conducting interviews:

- staff statements;
- reflective practice documents;
- staff members' aide-memoires or personal accounts;
- the incident form plus the local manager's initial investigation findings; and
- notes of any local management/team leader interviews with staff.

Statements and personal aide-memoires

As previously stated all staff involved in, and witness to, the incident should be asked to make as full a record as they can of the incident (including events leading up to and following the incident) as soon as possible . Whilst memory recall is recognised to be good following very traumatic adverse events, often the detail of the sequence of events and what else was happening in the environment can be lost. Local managers and team leaders are best placed to make sure this early record is made.

Where it is recognised that the organisation may have to involve the police or legal representatives, or be subject to an external investigation, formal witness statements should always be obtained as near to the time of the incident as is practical. All organisations should have formal guidelines on statement writing that are approved by their legal advisers. At minimum, staff need to understand that a formal statement:

- must state who the author is, their job title, their professional registration number, and the length of time in post;

- must contain more detail than what has been recorded in the patient or client record. The statement must address:
  - what "I" did and the rationale for this (i.e. why);
  - what "I" said;
  - why "I" omitted to do things;
  - what "I" heard;
  - what "I" was instructed to do or not do;
  - what "I" saw;
- must end with a truth statement. That is "everything I have written is true to the best of my knowledge and belief"; and
- must be dated and signed with the name of the author printed clearly.

Interagency investigations

Where there is coroner or police involvement, try and gain early agreement regarding the process and whether there are any opportunities for streamlining the process. For example, is it possible for the police and the health/social care investigation team to jointly interview staff? Is it possible for statements to be shared across agencies?

Within local areas where agencies know that they co-manage care, it is sensible if those organisations develop a memorandum of understanding, or each has a section in their incident investigation policies about investigations involving/affecting third parties. This section should be agreed between all agencies and read the same in all policies. Furthermore each of the organisations should have a defined person (identifiable by job title and department) who will act as the contact/reference point whenever there is consideration of the need for a multi-agency investigation. The contact points should be identified in each organisation's incident management/investigation policies.

For multi-agency investigations the optimal approach is one investigation team, comprising representation from the relevant agencies. This is preferable to each agency doing its own investigation in isolation and then bringing all of the data together. Greater robustness can be achieved by conducting it on a multi-agency basis to start with. NB: Please note that such an approach needs to be well managed and led by someone who knows what they are doing, i.e. an experienced investigator. The author considers that IMR's could be better delivered if conducted to these principles.

Note: The Department of Health (DH) published a document called *Memorandum of understanding: investigating patient safety incidents involving unexpected death or serious untoward harm* in February 2006. Whenever a serious incident occurs and there are also investigations required by the police, the Health and Safety Executive and/or the coroner, then this publication should be referred to.
It can be accessed at:
http://www.dh.gov.uk/en/Publicationsandstatistics/Publications/PublicationsPolicyAndGuidance/DH_4129918

2. From the PLACE (environment) in which the event occurred

Gathering information from the locality in which an incident occurred can be very important. For example if a mental health service user absconds from a secure environment, in the immediate aftermath schematics need to be made, photographs of the environment may need to be taken, and a safety inspection organised. Ideally this information needs to be gathered while the environment is "as it was" at the time the incident occurred. Trying to gather this information accurately days, weeks or months after the incident is far less effective owing to changes that may have occurred in the environment. For example, a safety solution may have been implemented.

For "single point in time" incidents in particular, getting out to the scene of the incident quickly to collect field data is an essential function of any or all of the following:

- the service management team;
- the risk management department;
- the health and safety team; and
- the estates department.

There should be clear guidance on how this type of information should be gathered within the organisation's incident reporting and management policy.

This activity is not something that should wait until a serious incident investigation is commissioned.

Information that can be gathered by the investigator or investigation team "from the place" may include:

- observations about how people go about their tasks and functions using techniques such as "non-participant observation"; and
- asking an experienced member of the relevant team to walk the investigation team through a system or process on location, on a "step by step" basis. This works very well to gain a detailed insight into systems and processes that are operational in laboratories such as microbiology, histopathology and haematology. It also works well in theatre suites and pharmacies, or ECT (electro-convulsive therapy) suites.

If possible the investigation team should try and visit the environment during a similar time period to that in which the incident occurred. For example, if the incident occurred at 10pm there may be reduced value in visiting the department at 2pm. One is unlikely to gain a true perspective of the environment as it related to the incident.

Making the most of site/field visits

The following prompts will assist you in making the most of such visits:

- Make observations about the layout of the environment. Make a sketch of the area, its layout and the position of furniture, equipment and people at the time of the event, noting the time of day, how busy it is with visitors, etc.
- Consider taking photographs. Digital photographs are now much more acceptable and commonplace. However, if the photographs may be used in a court case the authenticity of the photographs will need to be validated. Consequently ensuring that they are date and time stamped and maintaining a log of when the photo was taken and printing a copy in addition to storing it electronically is sensible. Photographic information is useful for:
  - recording and identifying environmental risk factors - e.g. general layout, points of potential danger, poor ergonomic design, blind spots, etc; and
  - recording the steps in a highly controlled process such as the processing of blood products, urine specimens, tissue samples etc.

3. From any PARTS (equipment, objects, moving parts etc) involved

Any piece of equipment, or any implement directly involved in an incident, should be removed and preserved. If it needs to be returned into service, this should not occur until it has been safety checked. Often the organisation's health and safety adviser will be able to assist and advise about this. Examples of the range of equipment you might retain are:

- medical equipment such as syringe pumps, wheelchairs, a theatre bed, diathermy equipment;
- fire hydrant;
- kitchen knife;
- computer hard drive;
- bleep; or a
- cardiotocograph machine (a monitor for recording a baby's heart rate in relation to uterine contractions in labour.)

A rule with work based equipment is "preservation of the evidence". Unless the police or coroner's officers require the physical evidence, the investigation team must ensure that all physical evidence is clearly labelled and preserved where possible. (If the object is required for a coroner's hearing or other agency, such as the police, at least retain photographic evidence).
The MHRA says in section 5 of its Device Bulletin called *Reporting adverse incidents and disseminating medical device alerts*, February 2010:
'www.mhra.gov.uk/Publications/Safetyguidance/DeviceBulletins/CON068594'

"Medical devices that have been involved in an incident should be quarantined.
Until the MHRA has been given the opportunity to carry out an investigation, they should not be:

- discarded
- repaired
- returned to the manufacturer.

All material evidence, i.e. devices/parts removed, replaced or withdrawn from use following an incident, instructions for use, records of use, repair and maintenance records, packaging materials, or other means of batch identification **must** be:

- clearly identified and labelled
- stored securely.

Evidence should not be interfered with in any way except for safety reasons or to prevent its loss. Where appropriate, a record should be made of all readings, settings and positions of switches, valves, dials, gauges and indicators, together with any photographic evidence and eyewitness reports."

4. PAPER evidence
Paper records often make up the bulk of information available to an investigation team following patient safety incidents and safeguarding incidents relating to children and vulnerable adults. As already indicated, for other incident types there may not be readily available informative documented records.

Where there is a rich source of written information available, the investigation team may wish to conduct an early analysis of this. An activity such as creating a detailed chronological or tabular timeline can be very beneficial in enabling the investigation team to achieve greater insight as to:

- the appropriateness of the terms of reference provided;
- what happened;
- what appears to have been done well; and
- what the early concerns are.

Examples of the sorts of written information that may be available to you during the early phases of the investigation process are:

- practice/process guidelines, policy and procedures;
- audit information;
- clinical/case management records;
- risk management audits;
- health and safety audits;
- incident reports;
- claims statistics;
- letters of concern written by staff;
- risk alerts;
- medical equipment maintenance records, purchase orders etc; and
- any correspondence from the patient/client or their representative(s).

5. From PARADIGMS, i.e. "that's the way we do things around here".
It is important in eliciting the general custom and practice of a working environment to speak to persons uninvolved in the event, who either normally work in the department or who have regular contact with it. The information obtained can help you shape the context in which factors leaving an area vulnerable to incidents have come to pass, e.g.:

- What is the custom and practice of the department?
- What is the prevailing attitude?
- How are things normally done?
- Are there any relationship difficulties amongst staff?

Collecting information relating to culture and custom and practice can be achieved via a variety of approaches. The following are suggestions:

- non-participant observer work;
- focus groups;
- semi-structured questionnaires;
- one-to-one interviews; and
- interviewing patients, service users, and customers.

Personal reflection by the author

Since taking responsibility for the investigation of serious incidents as an NHS employee and latterly as an independent investigator, I have always found it invaluable to create a detailed timeline of the sequence of events leading to an incident and the post-incident sequence of events if appropriate. Sometimes the timeline may be sparse because there is not very much information to hand, sometimes it is very detailed and information rich because it relates to an incident where the patient/child/client has a long history of contact with a range of health and/or social care providers. The variety in completeness of the timeline is not problematic, as more often than not the "first pass" timeline enables me to have much more clarity about:

- the core questions that must be asked during the investigation process;
- the systems and processes I need to understand better;
- the range of people I may need to speak with, and also any site visits that I may need to make.

I am convinced that one of the reasons Consequence UK delivers effective investigations is because we pay close attention at an early stage to analysing the written record before thinking about the overall direction of the investigation. We always create a tabular and not a simple timeline. This enables the notation of:

- the date, time and what was happening;
- any contextual information that may be relevant to what was happening at that time on that day;
- what appears to have been conducted appropriately and to expected local and/or national standards;
- areas of early concern. That is, the records do not demonstrate that the care and/or process has been conducted appropriately and to expected local and/or national standards;
- the wide range of questions associated with each time, or date, boundaried section of the timeline, and who the questions may need to be posed to.

Constructing this type of timeline does take longer than a simple chronological timeline. However, it is the experience of Consequence UK that it does deliver a more structured and complete investigation process.

2.2.2 Maintaining orderly information

Investigations tend to generate a large amount of information. Therefore it is important that the investigator (or investigation team) has a methodical approach to how the information is logged and stored when it is received. This sounds very straightforward. However, when one is conducting an investigation and juggling the "day job" as well, it is not always easy to be as organised as one should be.
You may want to set up a spreadsheet with core data fields on it that help maintain a register of documents. The following table represents one example of this.

Case Name:

Case Reference Number:

Document Reference No. (i.e. unique I.D. number)	Information Requested	From Whom	When Requested ?	Date Received	Placed Where	Returned to	Date
001/2001	Medical Records	Ward X	Date	25/06/01	Cabinet A	Med rec's	25/07/01
002/2001	Nursing Records	Ward X	Date	30/06/01	Cabinet B	Dr Aspen	25/07/01
003/2001	Copy of Incident form	Health & Safety Dept	Date	Date	Location		
004/2001	Witness Statement	Jo Bloggs	Date	Date	Location		

Maintaining such a log will assist you in staying on top of the investigation paperwork, avoid the hunt for "lost" records stopping at your door, and assist in the process of cross referencing and validation necessary in all robust investigations. Diligently maintaining a log of all information gathered will also assist you when you write your investigation report. All investigation reports will contain a section where the information used to inform the report's findings are listed. If you have maintained such a log from the start, completing this section of your report is made easier.

2.3 Detailed guidance on creating a chronology of events

As highlighted in Chapter 1, the chronology of events is of utmost importance in your investigation. The method you choose for mapping it out will affect the ease with which you can visualise the chain of events, and identify areas where further information gathering is required. The mapped chronology should also enable you to identify quite clearly the key problem areas, and areas of acceptable/good practice.
The following pages detail two common methods for mapping the incident chronology. Whichever one you use as an investigation team, you must ensure that the chronology shows:

- clarity of information; and
- sufficient level of detail especially at critical stages in the story line.

2.3.1 The narrative chronology

This style of mapping information is one with which you will be familiar. It is akin to what you see in novels and read in the newspaper. Essentially a narrative chronology tells a story. If you use this style, careful consideration must be given to the intended audience and the end to which this type of chronology is being employed. The breadth and depth of detail provided should be proportional to the significance of the information documented in relation to the event being examined. For example if the incident being analysed relates to a mental health homicide and there is no sexual element to what happened, focusing on issues relating to the sexuality of the service user would neither be appropriate nor proportional. A common complaint about the narrative chronology is that the lack of attention to formatting can lead a lack of clarity regarding the date(s) on which different events occurred. For some people the narrative chronology can be too "wordy".

An example of a narrative chronology

Example one: A patient who absconded from the psychiatric intensive care unit (PICU) in a mental health hospital

On 17 March at approximately 09.15, a patient was reported missing from the secure unit. The morning staff had reportedly been busy doing the drug round and accompanying the consultants on their ward round at the time the alarm was raised. It was the support worker allocated to Patient A who raised the alarm when he could not find patient A. The staff conducted a search of the grounds and the building. They could not find Patient A so they activated the missing person procedure, and contacted the police. They gave the police a description of the service user and also an outline of the risk he posed to himself and the public. Later that morning a member of the nursing team contacted the wife of Patient A. She was apparently asked to make contact with the PICU if her husband made contact with her. It was known that there had been some concerns over domestic violence in the past. Mid-morning the police contacted the PICU to advise that Patient A had been arrested at his marital home following a violent incident. He had attacked his wife with a knife. The police reported that Patient A had then attempted suicide. Patient A, the PICU was informed, had been taken into custody where he was awaiting a psychiatric assessment.

Comment

The narrative chronology above is short and easy to digest. However if one imagines a narrative chronology spanning some five to twenty pages there may be a loss of clarity using the presentation style (formatting) above. Furthermore, although short the narrative chronology presented does not contain some of the specific information one might like to know. For example, at what time did the PICU staff contact the police? What precisely did the PICU staff tell the police about Patient A's risk factors? Did the staff discharge their duty of care to Patient A's wife effectively? etc.

These are all questions one would wish to seek answers to during the investigation process. Where the chronology is short, it is unlikely that there will be a significant adverse impact on the quality of the investigation where the above style is used to recreate the sequence of events. However, where the chronology is long and/or complex, the risk of loss of focus for the investigation team, and omission of key questions that need to be asked during the investigation process, increases with the above format.

2.3.2 The simple chronology or timeline

A simple timeline usually makes explicit the date and time at each key step of a chronology. The example below shows a typical simple timeline. The information can be presented vertically or horizontally. The key features are the same.

Example two: the wrongly identified patient.

10/06/99 at 11.30am -The porters arrived to take Mrs J for a barium enema. The staff on the ward were not available to take the porter to Mrs. J so Staff Nurse N indicated that Mrs. J was in bed 3. (The nurse did not read the request card proffered by the porter).

10/06/99 at 11.35am -The porter took his wheelchair to bed 3 and told the patient he had come to take her to X-Ray. Mrs. J did not question this and did as she was requested.

10/06/99 at 11.40am - Mrs. J was received into the X-Ray department by an administrative clerk, who took the request card from the porter. Mrs J was told that the radiographer would be with her soon.

10/06/99 at 11.55am - Mrs. J was taken by a trainee radiographer through to the examination room, and helped on to the examination table and prepared for the procedure. At no time were her personal details checked.

10/06/99 at 12.05pm -The team were assembled and the procedure was about to commence when a radiographer noticed that the Christian name on Mrs J's wrist band was not what she was expecting. The request card was quickly checked and the staff realised they had the wrong patient.

10/06/99 at 12.10pm -The staff removed the rectal tubing from Mrs. J and told her that they had finished and that everything was fine. The trainee helped her back into her wheelchair and the porter took her back to the ward.

10/06/99 at 5.30pm - Mrs. J was visited by her husband and told him of her morning's activities. She also told him that she didn't think she had anything done, as no staff left the room and they usually do in X-Ray. He asked the staff nurse on duty what test his wife went for, as he wasn't aware that she needed anything else. He was then advised of the mix up of patients.

2.3.3 The tabular timeline

The tabular timeline is an alternative to the narrative chronology. It embraces some of the characteristics of the simple chronology in that it always identifies the date and time of each step in the antecedents to the incident, where this is known. However, the tabular timeline also contains a range of additional data fields. The essential data fields for a tabular timeline are:

- date, time, what was happening;
- contextual data, i.e. information that represents the depth of information or broader context;
- identified good or reasonable practice;
- questions the investigators have about "the case" and about systems and processes;
- the source of the data recorded (this enables a fully auditable process to be achieved); and
- the identity of the staff involved at each stage (noting name and grade can assist in planning the interviewing schedule).

An investigator may add to these fields depending on the nature of the investigation. For example if the investigation is a serious case review following serious harm to, or death of a child, the investigator(s) may wish to include additional fields on the timeline. For example:

- other agencies involved;
- relevant historical information;
- relevant family relationships and activities; and
- successful or unsuccessful contacts.

In a mental health incident additional fields might be:

- forensic history;
- risk taking behaviours;
- insight;
- medication; and
- successful and unsuccessful contacts.

Attention to detail at this stage of the investigation process will almost always pay dividends as one progresses through the investigation process.

It is the contention of the author that well mapped tabular timelines provide a greater degree of clarity about the key stages of the event chain, and the supporting contextual information. The tabular timeline is also useful if an investigation team wants to display the chronology and "view" the incident as a whole. The horizontal presentation of the tabular timeline makes it easy to read when displayed on a wall or around a room. This can facilitate the dynamic engagement of the staff involved in the incident, in contributing information to fill any knowledge or data gaps as an engaging reflective practice exercise. It can also enable teams of staff to better understand how an incident unfolded. Last but by no means least, presenting a tabular timeline to staff involved in the incident makes the whole investigation process transparent, and can support staff in trusting that the process is open and fair.

Note 1: The timeline is particularly valuable for viewing events involving multiple specialties or agencies, as it enables you to map, and therefore see, the interface between the involved agencies within a single document, rather than having to try and map this across four or five narrative chronologies or simple timelines. The use of colour and/or symbols may be useful when creating a multi-agency timeline to enable the input of each service to be clearly visualised.

Note 2: Where there are a number of similar incidents, the tabular timeline can be a useful tool for identifying a range of common emergent themes. This can be useful in achieving economies of scale across the investigation process.

Note 3: If the intention is to present a timeline to staff, care needs to be taken to ensure it does not inadvertently make staff feel they are being singled out or victimised. How the timeline is presented will influence its impact on staff.

What do other people say?

The author has led a significant number of investigation workshops since 2002. The consistent feedback received is that the tabular timeline is a very powerful tool. It enables the investigator to broaden their thinking about the event, and the questions they need to ask, unlike the narrative or simple chronology.

One individual said: "There are many areas where you can take shortcuts in the investigation process, however, the timeline is something I never shortcut. I have to do the timeline to enable me to take safe shortcuts."

Another said:
"The information collected for each event can be customised to suit the nature of the incident and the investigation. The timeline facilitates analysis, i.e. the identification of trends, clusters of issues/CDPs/SDPs/causation factors, links between issues (cause and effect). It is a very efficient (LEAN) method of outlining the events and issues for the benefit of the investigation team, the wider team for group work and the commissioner/report reader. It is a versatile tool which can be adapted for many purposes (complaints, disciplinaries, grievances, hearings). In my organisation many health and social care staff have commented on the usefulness of the tabular timeline for post incident team reflection meetings. It does seem to provide a means by which all present can become engaged in a supportive manner."

2.3.4 Mapping and building the timeline

One usually maps the data in a horizontal or vertical template with arrows dictating the flow of time. From a visual perspective, and from a reader's perspective, the author has always found horizontal to work best.

There are some core givens when mapping any timeline. These are:

- Decide what point in the care/case management pathway you are starting from. Make sure you cover a sufficient time period to enable you to properly understand the antecedents and not just the incident itself.
- If there is more than one professional/agency involved, start with the agency/professional that has had most contact or involvement. Map the chronology initially using those records. You could call this the "first pass timeline".
- When working with multiple sets of records, once the first pass timeline is complete, then take the next set of records containing information about the case management or care pathway and intersperse this on a chronological basis. This is where using a spread sheet is invaluable. It is so easy to add a row of data.
- Think about the data fields you want. Will a standardised timelining template suit you/your organisation, or do you need something that can be adapted to the unique needs of the case? Whatever data fields you use, the timeline should support your forensic analysis of the case records.

The following list details what we would consider to be the core elements of any tabular timeline:

- Information source: where did the information that you are putting on your timeline come from? E.g. "Clinical records folder 1, correspondence section".
- Date (and time where possible).
- The chronology: what was happening at this step in the chronology.
- Contextual information: information that is relevant to this step in the chronology, if this data is available. E.g. how busy was it, what were the staffing levels and skill mix, etc.
- Good/acceptable practice: is there anything noteworthy for positive feedback?
- Concerns: are you reading anything of concern professionally? For example: "The risk assessment contains no qualitative description of past risky behaviours and the circumstances of these, even though it indicates that there has been past risk of harm to others and/or self. There is no documented relapse prevention or contingency plan."
- Questions about the case management/care management: this is for questions specific to the incident and patient care or case management. Consequently there may be a predominance of questions about what staff were doing, how and why.
- Questions about the system of work: these are questions more relating to the middle circle on the Wheel of Misfortune. They cover clinical leadership, supervision, training, availability of guidelines, custom and practice. These will assist an investigation team in having a balanced understanding of staff members' actions or omissions.

2.3.5 Generating questions as you map an incident's chronology

During the process of creating the timeline it is good practice to notate all questions that you think off as they arise. The answers to some of your questions may be found as you progress through the case records, but many questions may remain unanswered. Those questions that remain unanswered will need to be considered for their relevance to the terms of reference and their importance to the delivery of a safe and effective service. During this consideration process the range of questions may be grouped and themed, and some may be discarded because on reflection they are considered to be too pedantic, or not appropriate.

During the process of creating the timeline and notating questions, you may want to consider making a double record of these:

- one record on the timeline itself, this is particularly easy if you are using an Excel spreadsheet as your master timeline document. The benefit of doing this is that you have a master document; and
- one record on a separate piece of paper cross referenced with its exact location on the timeline. For example if you are using a spreadsheet, and the question is a replica of that notated at Row 10, then this would be your cross reference. (Note: One question to one piece of paper)

This diligence gives you a completely auditable process, which is important if anyone has to quality assure the investigation process. It also means that you can easily group and theme the questions asked. Typically you will have two main thematic groups with, or without, relevant sub groups. For example:

- Theme 1: Questions directly relevant to the case management.
- Theme 2: Questions about wider systems and processes.
- Theme 1a: Questions relating to the risk assessments conducted and the documentation of these.
- Theme 1b: Questions relating to medication management or communications with other agencies, etc.

2.3.6 Challenges and the tabular timeline

There are challenges with the timeline. The three that crop up most frequently are:

- To what degree of detail should one map the timeline?
- How much time should it take?
- Who should create it?

What level of detail?

The purpose of creating a timeline is to enable you to have a good understanding of the sequence of events. You may be reporting at various stages of your investigation to a quality assurance group, and/or you may want to share the timeline with staff involved in the incident and the persons affected by the incident. Therefore it needs to be reasonably detailed.

It is better to take small steps through the chronology rather than big steps. Essentially, you are unlikely to come unstuck by going into too much detail. The timeline is the building block of your investigation. It gives your investigation its firm foundation. If you are not diligent enough with what you record at this stage, you are more at risk of not delivering a robust investigation than someone who does pay more attention to the detail.

It is not uncommon to have a number of timeline entries on a single day if there was a lot going on in that day. Similarly it is not unusual in an investigation spanning a number of weeks, months or years for a timeline to display data gaps. The reason for data gaps should always be highlighted. For example: "1 June 2010 – 31 July 2010: `The plan of care remained unchanged and nothing remarkable occurred over this period.'"

How much time?

The length of time it takes to create a timeline can be affected by a range of variables:

- the amount of documentary information available, and the orderly presentation of this;
- the familiarity of the investigation team with the methodology of timelining; and
- the time span requiring timelining.

The variables that will most frequently increase the time required are one's familiarity with the task and the relative completeness of the documentary information. For example, if one has a copy set of clinical records and it transpires that one side of each sheet of clinical records only has been copied this will decrease efficiency and increase the time required for the task.

The following points will enable the most efficient use of time set aside for the timelining activity:

- the collation and orderly presentation of all essential written records;
- clinical/case records need to be presented as if they were the originals. You are looking at what the clinicians/caseworkers would have been looking at.
- set aside dedicated time for reviewing the records and creating the timeline. It is important that this is time where you will not be disturbed. Your phone should be off and your email closed. Efficiency for this task requires focused attention.
- Where possible have two investigation team members working side by side to create the timeline. Ideally this will be the investigative lead and one of the specialist advisers. You can create a

timeline on your own but we do not recommend it for serious incident investigations.

- Once you have familiarised yourself with the records, do not overly analyse them before commencing the timeline. It is generally not a good use of time as you must read them carefully to create the timeline.
- Stay focused on the terms of reference and the purpose of analysing the documentation. It is easy to have discussions with colleagues about what might have happened, and to try and elucidate this from the data you have. However such discussions are often time ill spent. The only way to find out what happened is to have clarity about what you know. Everything else is a question.

Author's comment
I am frequently asked how long people should set aside for creating the timeline. There is no definitive response to this. As an outline guide I would suggest the following:

- For non-complex cases where the chronology is six months' worth of data or less, a half day should enable you to create a reasonably robust timeline providing that you have all preparation activities in hand.
- For investigations where you need to map between one and three years' worth of data, my experience is that you need to think of between one and two days.
- For investigations with an antecedent chronology of greater than three years but less than ten years, you need to think carefully about the period that requires a detailed analytical timeline, and where a simple timeline will be sufficient.

Note 1: The above timescales apply to cases where there are up to two agencies or services involved. If there are three or more agencies involved you may need to increase the timescales accordingly.

Note 2: Please be mindful that the above time frames are a guide only, no two investigations are the same and with experience you will find that you will be better positioned to make accurate estimates of the time you need.

Timelining and time

If it takes a day or so to create a robust timeline at the start of an investigation, is that too much time if there has been a serious adverse outcome for a person who was being cared for, or protected by a health or social care system?

Note 3: Acute health sector cases should generally take less time than cases involving mental health, learning disabilities, and safeguarding cases. This is because the time periods one is reviewing are generally shorter and the records often do not span more than one agency. With mental health, learning disabilities and safeguarding cases the periods of time one is reviewing are often longer and it is not unusual for several agencies to be involved in the care and/or case management. Consequently these cases usually require more time.

Extract from a structured tabular timeline

Date: 07/05/2001 Time:

Event
Status Quo continues re. physical deterioration.

Supplimentary info
Assistance is required with bathing and dressing and mobility. Assessment showed Patient X walking to be not so good. Her appearance is also not so good she is sometimes disorderly. An OT assessment requested

Positive points
Stockton Assessment performed Scored 11 / 40 Referral to OT

Problems(CMP's & SDP's)

Further info required
1. What assistance was provided?
2. Was Patient X helped into and out of the bath.
3. Was Patient X asked to let staff know when she wanted a bath?
4. The Stockton Assessment is quite different to the previous two did anyone consider why this was?
5. Did carers at 'The Ward' have a one-to-one each month with the named nurse for Patient X, or her associate nurse.

Background Information

Additional service based questions
1. What is the Trust's strategy for increasing the involvement of carers?
2. What opportunities exist for carers to actively be engaged in the strategic direction of the organisation?

Date: 08/05/2000 Time: 19:30:00

Event
Calcium tablets found in Patient X's room

Supplimentary info
Patient X said she had been taking them but would give back to her husband. Dr C reviewed Patient X.

Positive points
Decision to review Patient X daily with SHO

Problems(CMP's & SDP's)

Further info required
1. If Patient X was able to bring these in and no-one knew what else might she have brought in?
2. Did anyone sit down with husband and make him aware so that other medicines at home could be locked away?
3. What was Patient X risk status at this time?

Background Information

Additional service based questions
1. What is the Trust's strategy for increasing the involvement of carers?
2. What opportunities exist for carers to actively be engaged in the strategic direction of the organisation?

Date: 09/05/2001 Time: 19:00:00

Event
Records show that Patient X mood remains low and that walking is a 'shuffle'

Supplimentary info
The notation at this time is very consistent. Patient X pattern of behaviour seems to be quite consistent, and unremarkable for her. However the issues underpinning her altered gait appear to be unexplored.

Positive points

Problems(CMP's & SDP's)
Apparent failure to explore reasons for altered gait

Further info required
Were the reasons underlying Patient X's altered gait explored?

Background Information

Additional service based questions
1. What manual handling assessment forms are in use in 'The Ward'
2. What training have staff had in manual handling assessment?
3. Does the Trust have a manual handling advisor
4. Is there a Trust training programme for manual handling

Example of a simple chronological timeline (with supporting explanatory text boxes)

8/07
Child admitted to hospital with behavioral problems

Supporting info.
e.g. Outline of admission process and completeness of documentation

11/07
Child destructive on ward asked to stay in own room.

Supporting info.
e.g. typical circumstances, trigger for behavior if any? etc

23/07
Child hostile towards staff.

Detail outline of processes and procedures undertaken

26/07-13/08
Multiple episodes of frustrated outbursts and seclusion.

Detail salient key points e.g. Clinical management review
Multi professional meeting etc.

14/07
Staff raise concerns over their ability to manage child

What action was taken? e.g. support to the staff etc

B

INCIDENT

B

16/08 7.00 am
Threw breakfast across dining room. Sent to room

Detail outline of processes and procedures.

16/08 7.40 am
Allowed to resocialise

Detail policy on resocialisation procedures

Child immediately runs down ward pushing other children aside. Staff follow shouting for him to return.

Key points?
e.g. how was physical approach made?
What was shouted?

The mother of another child is entering the ward and tries to intervene.

Detail of all that happened
What she said?
Tone of voice? etc

Child takes hold of nearby table fork and stabs parent.

Legend:

Event

connector

Supporting explanatory notes

Direction

2.4 Other approaches to mapping information

Although the timeline is a powerful data mapping and analysis tool, it is not the only approach. Investigators must take care not to use it exclusively when an alternative approach might be better.

The following details some alternative approaches to mapping information. These approaches can be used at an early stage in the investigation or as the investigation progresses, or at the information analysis stage when all information has been gathered.

2.4.1 Time person and contact grids

Time person and contact grids are a valuable mapping tool if you need to:

- clarify where various persons were during the incident scenario;
- map the pattern of contact between agencies and a vulnerable person over specified periods of time;
- map the pattern of contact between different professional groups within the same team or organisation;
- ascertain whether a member of staff accused of harming a patient was on duty over the periods of time in which the harm was said to have occurred, and who was most frequently around; and
- map the pattern of prescribing of medication.

They are simple to construct and can be constructed alongside the timeline. However, it seems to work best if the contact grid is constructed as a separate document to the timeline. Perhaps the most famous time person grid in UK health is that constructed by the police force investigating the Beverly Allitt case. Its mapping of the children harmed alongside the staff who were on duty on each occasion revealed a common individual - Beverly Allitt.
The sorts of scenarios where you might consider undertaking this type of mapping are the following:

- allegations of abuse or deliberate harm;
- missing controlled medications;
- absconded patients from a secure environment or whilst on close observations;
- complaints regarding bed moves;
- to assess continuity of care;
- to map the pattern of prescribing over a period of time; and
- to map the pattern of successful or unsuccessful contacts with services.

Author's comment

More often than not time person and contact grids can be mapped in a Word table or spreadsheet format. I have used them to:

- Plot the continuity of contact with a mental health service user over a five year period where there was a preconceived belief in an organisation that continuity was poor. The contact grid by professional group (consultant psychiatrist and community mental health nurse), revealed that the continuity of care by the community mental health nurses was good. It also revealed that the service user had one consultant psychiatrist for the first three of his five years' contact with the service. Furthermore the contact grid showed that the service user had been reviewed by his consultant psychiatrist on each outpatient appointment. The contact grid, however, also showed that in the last two years of contact, prior to the serious incident, the service user had two different consultant locum psychiatrists. The contact grid also showed that the service user was never reviewed by either consultant at outpatient appointments but was reviewed by senior house officers (SHOs) (junior doctors). Of the SHOs who reviewed the service user, the contact grid showed that only one reviewed the service user twice. The contact grid enabled a more balanced perspective in relation to continuity in his case management.

- Plot the medications for an elderly lady over a three year period using a bar graph. This showed quite clearly a cyclical pattern of prescribing for a woman who was considered treatment resistant. It also showed the gradual increase over time of the range of sedative medications she was prescribed.

A colleague used the methodology to create a map of staff placement when a mother alleged that a nurse working in paediatric intensive care was deliberately tampering with her child's respiratory equipment. What the contact grid revealed was that it was the child's mother who was tampering with her child's equipment. The mother was subsequently prosecuted.
Another colleague used the principles of the time person grid to present aggregated data from incident reports about increasing violence and aggression in a managed home for people with learning disabilities. Presenting the data pictorially enabled the staff to better understand what was going on and manage the situation appropriately.

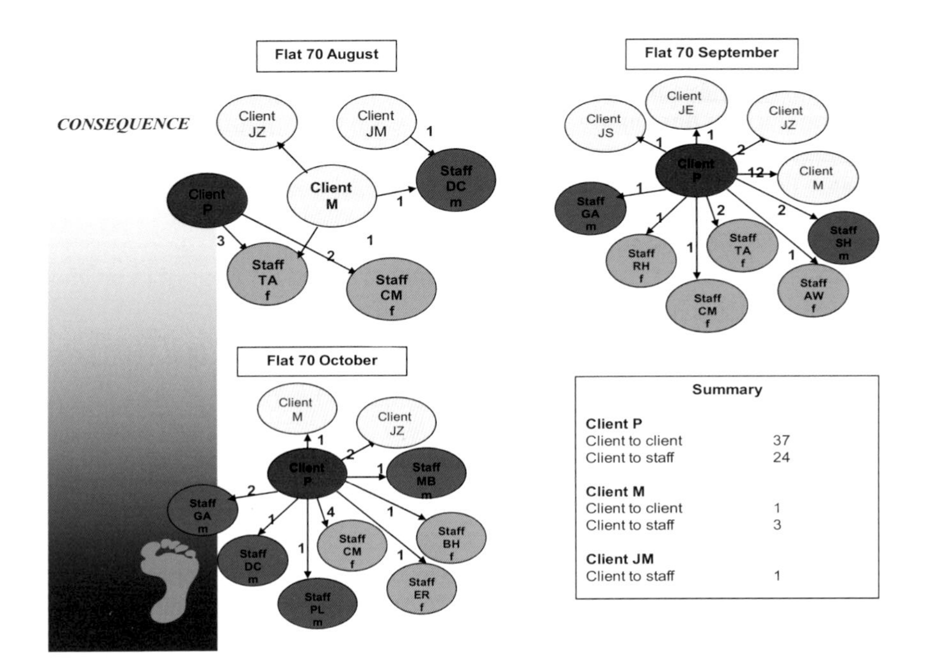

An example of a standard time person grid

This time person grid is based on an absconding service user who absconded and then committed suicide.

Type of Staff	9.00 am	9.15am	9.30am
SHO ‘A’	With patient ‘W’	In office	With patient ‘X’
Ward Manager	In office	In office	In office
Nurse ‘B’	At coffee	In office	In Day Room
Support Worker ‘C’	With patient ‘Y’	In kitchen	With patient ‘Y’

The example contact grid on the following page shows an extract from a simple timeline following a child death in the community, with a contact grid incorporated as an integral component. On reflection it would have been better to have created a separate document to present the pattern analysis of contacts.

An example of a simple timeline with a contact grid incorporated

Date	21/02/85	18/03/85	22/03/85	11/05/85 - 14/05/85	27/05/85
Event	1	2	3	4	5
Additional info.		SW aware of social circumstance	Client advised to contact CAB	Child 'A' seen at Child Health Clinic	More complaints. SW visit
Midwife			#		
Health visitor		#		#	
Social worker			#	#	#
Police				#	
Housing Dept.				#	
Ambulance					
Education					
Questions relating to fact based info and surrounding circumstance.	What is the policy for late bookers? Any form of risk assessment? Local policy followed?	What social circumstances? SW management report should clarify this.	Did this ever happen?	What were the communications between involved services?	Was this a planned appointment or on the spot appointment? Were the same or different SWs involved?

In this diagram symbols are used to show the attempts made by each individual service to gain access to Child X. Other issues of interest in a case such as this could be:

- the modes of communication between the various agencies involved; and
- the number of visits made to the child's place of residence with:
  - no access;
  - access but no examination of the child; and
  - access and examination of the child.

2.4.2 Change analysis

Change analysis has a valuable place in your incident investigation and RCA toolkit and maybe a more appropriate tool than the tabular timeline for some incidents. It can be used in conjunction with the complete range of tools presented in this manual, or on its own.
The sorts of scenarios that are suited to change analysis are:

- services such as NHS Direct;
- blood transfusion services;
- pharmacy dispensing services;
- histopathology;
- theatre suites e.g. the consent process, or the process for checking instruments and swabs;
- sterile services; and
- medicines administration and the prescribing of medication.

All of the above operate highly controlled processes. Incidents in these areas often occur because of some change in the process, whether this was intended or not, or because of missing control measures in the process.

Change analysis is not however confined to areas that operate highly controlled systems and processes. It can be used whenever an incident occurs where a task is carried out in a prescribed format, to determine if any alteration in the way it was conducted had an impact on the incident that occurred.

How to create a change analysis map

- Firstly, clarify the nature of the problem you want to analyse.
- Then map out the normal procedure as it was designed to be conducted.
- Alongside this, map out how the process or procedure was conducted on this occasion (i.e. prior to the incident).
- Then compare the two processes.
- Identify any differences between the designed process and how it was conducted.
- Reflect on the differences identified and consider whether the difference(s) had a direct causative impact on the incident that occurred.
- Analyse why these differences occurred. Observational techniques and the interviewing of staff may be required to achieve this.

A case example

Mrs A, who was forty-eight years of age, had gynaecology problems. Following all appropriate investigations, the histopathology reports clearly indicated the need for Mrs A to undergo a hysterectomy. The procedure was competently performed. On manual inspection, the surgeon thought the uterus looked healthy given the diagnosed carcinogenic changes found in histopathology. He sent the uterus off for histological examination, as was his normal practice. The histological examination revealed that there was no uterine carcinoma present and the hysterectomy performed had not been required. A review of the tissue samples examined in the histopathology department, on the same day as Mrs A's, revealed that a translocation error had occurred and the results attached to Mrs A actually belonged to an 81 year old woman.

The following diagram shows how change analysis can be used to conduct an efficient and effective investigation, for process incidents such as this.

A diagrammatic example of change analysis applied to the case of Mrs A

Normal procedure	Procedure carried out in Mrs A's case	Did the change cause the problem ?	How?
Uterine tissue samples taken	As per normal procedure	No change	
Samples sent to lab	As per normal procedure	No change	
Samples and investigation request cards placed in individual trays	A bundle of mixed samples collected and placed in a single tray	Yes	It provided the opportunity for samples and the accompanying request cards to become separated
Histopathologist examines samples individually on his/her examination table	Histopathologist takes a collection of samples onto his/her examination table	Yes	This change increased the risk of a translocation of tissue samples, and also of mixing request cards
The findings of examination are written on the back of the request card that corresponds to the sample examined. Unique identifier recorded on the back of request card	The findings of examination are written on the back of the request card that corresponds to the sample examined. Unique identifier not recorded on the back of request card	Yes	There is a control gap in the existing system. The non-requirement to record the unique identifier on the slide sample along with the histopathology findings meant there was a loss of opportunity to identify the error
Secretary types up the results, cross checking unique identifiers on the front and back of the request card	Secretary types up the results, no cross check made of the unique identifiers on the front and back of the request card	Yes	
Surgeon accepts histopathology report in good faith and performs required operation	Surgeon accepts histopathology report in good faith and performs required operation	No change. But the routine acceptance of the findings in spite of his/her surprise at the result did contribute to the incident	

Once the lapses in processes and any absences in control measures have been identified, the investigator may need to undertake further information gathering and analysis of how and why the procedural changes occurred. Appendix 1 sets out a range of methodologies that could assist with this, including control analysis.

The investigation process

Step three:

Information Gathering – collecting the answers to your questions and conducting the initial analysis of the information

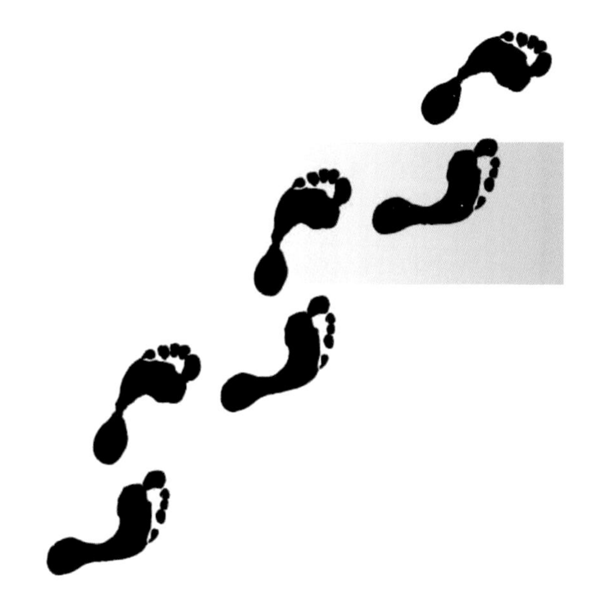

3.0 Introduction

This is a major part of the investigation process, and the competence with which it is carried out will directly impact on the final findings, conclusions and recommendations made.

The avenues for collecting the range of information required include:

- local and national policies and procedures;
- internet searches;
- professional journal articles;
- professional colleges' published guidance and standards;
- data gathered by observing staff going about their work in key stages of the care management or case management process. For example shadowing a ward round, or a drug round; and
- interviewing staff, individually and/or in groups.

Whatever information sources are used, there is an expectation that these will be listed in an appropriate appendix of the investigation report.

Author's comment
Some investigations are undertaken on the basis of a case notes analysis alone. For any serious incident, including serious case reviews, this is insufficient. A case notes analysis:

- will give an indication as to the reasonableness of the case/care management;
- will help an investigator determine what areas need to be focused on in an investigation;
- may tell the investigator that there appears to be no significant area, or areas of concern and that there is no value in progressing the investigation. This is especially so where there is rigorous adherence to the principle of proportionality.

Where there are significant concerns about case/care management based on documentation review, halting the investigation at this stage and conducting no further information or evidence gathering means that the investigator (or investigation team) draws its conclusions on an incomplete and potentially flawed understanding of what happened and why. Not only is this undesirable, but may result in recommendations that are wrongfully directed and that achieve no improvement in quality and safety, and may potentially impede quality and safety improvements.

Where a case notes analysis alone is conducted, the investigator can only report on what is found in the notes. He/she can say where the notes contain evidence supporting compliance with accepted standards of practice. He/she can also say where there is a lack of documentary evidence. What he/she cannot say is that any gaps in documentation translate into lapses in practice. The only way this can be determined is by talking to the persons involved.

Because talking to people provides such a rich information source, this chapter focuses on the investigative interview. It is during the interview scenario that the investigation team really gets to grips with the case, and starts to understand what happened, how and why.

3.1 The investigative interview

Essential preparation work

Knowing the case

To plan for an effective and efficient interview the investigator, or team, needs to be well prepared. This means that they need to know the incident chronology, and any standards of practice that were relevant to the case/patient management at the time. If a robust timeline has been created, the investigator(s) should have a good understanding of the chronology. Making sure that all relevant policies and procedures have been assimilated, or at least key elements of them read and tagged, should enable appropriate familiarity with local and national practice standards.

Collecting triangulated and validated data

It is important at the end of the information gathering process that investigators can triangulate and validate the information they have gathered. Using a validation map to ensure that the same range of questions are being posed to at least two, preferably three to four interviewees can assist in maximising the opportunity for triangulated and validated data.

A validation and triangulation map is no more complicated than a X/Y chart. Along one axis one places the question numbers, or thematic groups of questions, or questions themselves. Along the other axis the investigators list the individuals it believes need to be interviewed. Then the investigators map the questions to be asked against each interviewee's name. The investigators then look at the chart to see that there are at last two or more interviewees per question/theme (see example below).

A validation map is also helpful in identifying potential interviewees for whom you have identified no questions, and also questions for which you have not identified the right interviewees.

Example validation map 1:

	Admission Process	Risk Assessment	Medicines Administrations	The sequence of events on 4 July	Clinical supervision
Cons 1	✓	✓			
Nurse 1		✓	✓	✓	✓
Nurse 2	✓	✓	✓		✓
Team Leader	✓	✓	✓		✓
GP	✓				
Support worker A				✓	
Support worker B				✓	

Example validation map 2:

	Questions 1-3	Questions 4-7	Questions 8-10	Questions 11-12	Question 13
Cons 1	✓	✓			
Nurse 1		✓	✓	✓	✓
Nurse 2	✓	✓	✓		✓
Team Leader	✓	✓	✓		✓
GP	✓				
Support worker A				✓	
Support worker B				✓	

The interview aide-memoire

Once the investigator has set out an interview validation and triangulation map, an aide-memoire can be created for each interview. The alternative would be, to print the validation map, and append to it the questions to which the question numbers relate. This would also act as a quick reference guide during an interview.

Informing/preparing interviewees

All employees have a duty to support the investigation process, so opting out is not an option. However, how the investigators engage with interviewees can influence the mind set with which they attend for interview.

The following can help:

- Early contact with the manager, or team leader of a service to explain the investigation process, so that he/she can act as a reference point for interviewees and offer reassurance.
- Providing the manager, or team leader, with a copy of the type of confirmation letter, or email, his/her staff will receive so that he/she can share this with staff.
- Agreeing at an early stage the interview period with the local manager/team leader so that on duty arrangements can be attended to well in advance. Also this enables the investigators to be informed at an early stage if staff have already booked annual leave.
- Providing the manager/team leader with information about the investigation process and what staff can expect. (All organisations should have an information leaflet for staff about "What it means if you are called to interview for an internal RCA investigation", or similar.)
- Having a standardised letter template which sets out all of the core information that should be provided to an interviewee (clearly if there is an information leaflet this could be quite a short letter).

Information required by all interviewees

1. Who are you and what are you doing?
2. Why do you want to meet with me?
3. What are the terms of reference for the investigation?
4. Who will be interviewing me?
5. Can I bring a professional friend or union representative?
6. Where and when will my interview be? And how long will it last?
7. How will the interview record be used and who will see it?
8. How will the interview record be made, and will I get a chance to validate it?
9. Will I get to read the draft report and can I comment on it?
10. If I am criticised do I have the right to see the evidence upon which the criticism is made?

The venue for conducting interviewees

The location for conducting interviews is important, but perhaps not as important as some tend to think. The preparation of the interviewee in terms of the provision of good information, and the way the interviewee is treated in an interview is far more important than the location and layout of the room.

Ideally, investigative interviews will be held in:

- a quiet room away from the normal working environment;
- a room that enables optimal placement of any required tables and chairs;
- a room near to facilities for making refreshments;
- a room near to a toilet;
- a room with a discrete waiting area;
- a room with good natural light; and
- a location where parking is easy.

Of the above the most important are:

- a quiet location;
- near to refreshment facilities;
- a waiting area;
- a room with good natural light; and
- easy parking if staff are expected to travel.

Effective interviews can be conducted in rooms that do not meet optimal layout standards without impeding the process at all, if everything else is done right.

The investigation team and who is doing what

It is often not necessary for all members of an investigation team to be present at all interviews. If the investigators are well prepared, and appropriate thought has been given to who are the best team members to conduct each interview, then it is possible to achieve an interview team of two persons. One person will be leading the interview and the other person will take responsibility for making the notes of the interview and acting as back up to the main interviewer.

Generally speaking the person leading the interview should be the investigator with the most relevant experience and/or professional background to the interviewee. Therefore if you are interviewing a consultant histopathologist, it is ideal if the interviewer is also a consultant histopathologist. If you are interviewing a mental health nurse then it is ideal if the interviewer has up-to-date mental health nursing experience.

If it is not possible to match the skills and experience of the interviewers to the interviewees, it is essential that the investigation team, and in particular the interviewer, gains some knowledge in the relevant field. In the case of the consultant histopathologist, this might involve visiting the histopathology department to gain an appreciation of what happens in that department, or seeking information from the Royal College of Pathologists.

However an investigation team chooses to conduct its interviews, at absolute minimum the roles of those to be present at an interview must be agreed. This includes the responsibility for taking the notes of the interview.

If there is no member of the investigation team competent to take good quality interview notes, then consideration should be given to obtaining support from someone who can touch type, and who is used to taking dictation. It is essential that a good quality record of the interview is made.

Author's comment

The quality of notes taken during the interview will directly affect the quality of the investigation report and the validity of an investigation team's findings and recommendations. If poor quality interview notes are taken then there will be a poor quality analysis, and a poor quality report. An investigation team should be able to validate everything presented in the findings section of its investigation report. This is only possible with good quality interviewing and good quality interview records.

It is accepted that few persons involved in internal investigations will have the expertise of a stenographer; nevertheless it should be possible to capture a lot of good quality information with good keyboard skills and also with clear demarcation of roles in the investigation team. Effective utilisation of the "reflect back" technique, explained below, during an interview will also enhance the note taker's ability to achieve good quality notes.

The interview day

Before the interviewees arrive

- Get there early, make sure room layout is as good as it can be;
- make sure there are tissues available;
- make sure there is a jug of water and glasses;
- make sure you have a sign to put on the door if near to a public thoroughfare that says something like "Interview in Progress, Quiet Please";
- make sure you know where the loos are;
- make sure there are seats outside the door for interviewees to sit on while they are waiting;
- open a window if the room is stuffy;
- set up any equipment required, such as laptop for taking notes, and/or recording equipment if this is being used;
- set out any case notes or clinical records and display the timeline if you are using it; and
- settle yourself. Have everything you need at hand, including your aide-memoire for the interview.

Welcoming the interviewee

- Invite the interviewee into the interview room;
- introduce everyone in the room and offer water and/or tea/coffee;
- make sure the interviewee knows where the toilet is;
- make sure the interviewee is comfortable with where they are sitting;
- if the interviewee has come on their own, make sure that this is what they want;
- check that the interviewee has received any information that you have previously sent and that they have read it;
- ask the interviewee if they have had opportunity to refresh their recollection of the clinical/case records; and
- once settled, read the standardised introduction you have prepared for all interviewees.

Note: If an interviewee involved in the case management tells you that they have not read any of the case/clinical records, reassure them that the records are in the interview room and that they have the opportunity to refresh their memory at any stage during the interview process.

The main body of the interview

This is the stage in the interview where the bulk of information will be shared, the nature and style of the questions asked is therefore important. Be mindful of the person taking notes; speak clearly and at a sensible pace.

Ideally, you will:

- Start with a "tell all instruction". For example: "Maria, you were the named nurse for Patient X. Tell me everything you can remember about her from when you first met her on the 5 December to the incident that occurred on the 10 December." Or: "Peter, you were the social worker for Miss A for the last five years. Talk me through your recollections of her, and her ability to care for, and protect her children over that time." Or: "Jane, you have been working with the XYZ team since 2001. Tell us about your experiences of working with the team since that time, to the current day. It will be helpful if you can share with us things about the team that have remained constant over that period as well as things that have changed. Just tell us everything you can remember, don't feel that any information is too small or insignificant, we would like to hear it all."

- When the interviewee has said all they have to say (without interruptions from the investigators), it is a good idea to reflect back to the interviewee what you think you have heard and understood. This is a very powerful interview technique. It allows the interviewee to confirm that you have understood correctly, and also where you have not. It also enables the person taking the notes to ensure that they have captured accurately the content and context of the discussion.

- Following on from the free recall period the interviewer may decide to focus on particular aspects of the information shared, and explore things in more depth. These questions should as far as possible be "open" questions. For example: "Peter, you said that caring for her children had always been challenging for Miss A. Tell me more about that." It is also important, that wherever possible the interviewer tries to order his/her questions in the order of the chronology as recounted by the interviewee. This can help with an interviewee's memory recall.

- You may also need to ask closed questions to clarify certain points. For example: “Peter, you said that Miss A achieved sufficient parenting skills in 2005, so that her last child was not subject to a care order. Have I understood correctly?”

- Once your exploration of the interviewee’s recall of the case management/person/child etc is complete, then you do need to reflect on any outstanding areas you have identified for exploration. It is sensible to systematically work through these. Interviewees will generally welcome some overview of how you are going to address this part of the interview and the range of topics to be addressed (Note: you should have already advised them of this in your pre-interview letter).

Author’s comment

1. Remember to use the reflect back technique regularly throughout the interview process. It is an invaluable tool. An example of this is: “Jane, my understanding of you have just said is .... Have I interpreted you correctly?”

2. Remember to maintain contact with the note taker. Make sure the note keeper feels comfortable to ask you to slow down, or repeat a short section, and to say when they do not understand what is being said. If the note taker does not understand something, then it is likely that potential readers of the investigation report will not understand either. Effective team working provides the opportunity for technical information to be explained in plain language during the interview process and minimises the risk of misinterpretation.

The need for time out during the main body of the interview

During the interview process the investigator does need to be sensitive to the interviewee’s potential need for time out and a break. If an interview is likely to exceed an hour, then a break should be offered after an hour. Interviews are exhausting for everyone present, but most exhausting for the interviewee. Refreshments should be offered at this time.

Closure of the interview

Once all areas to be explored have been addressed it is time to bring the interview to a close. There are some important components that need to be addressed at this stage:

- The interviewee needs to be asked if they have anything else they’d like to add, or any questions for the interviewers.
- The interviewee needs to be informed about what will happen now. For example, when will he/she get a copy of their interview notes? Can he/she amend the interview record in any way, and if yes, how? When is the investigation likely to be completed? Will he/she get to read the draft report and comment on it? If he/she is criticised will he/she have the right of redress in keeping with Salmon principles (see point 2 in the box below).
- It is good practice to ask the interviewee if they are OK, and to remind them of any independent sources of support the organisation offers.
- It is good practice to find out how interviewees found their interview experience. This, however, is probably best achieved when they are sent their interview notes, rather than at the end of their interview.
- The interviewee should be provided with the contact details for the investigation team leader in case they think of anything else they would have liked to have communicated.
- It is good practice to return the conversation to the “everyday” before sending the interviewee on their way.

The Salmon principles (The Tribunals & Inquiries Act, 1921)

1. Before any person becomes involved in an inquiry, the Tribunal must be satisfied that there are circumstances which affect him and which the Tribunal proposes to investigate.
2. Before any person who is involved in an inquiry is called as a witness, he should be informed of any allegations which are made against him and the substance of the evidence in support of them.
3. (a) He should be given an adequate opportunity of preparing his case and of being assisted by his legal advisers. (b) His legal expenses should normally be met out of public funds.
4. He should have the opportunity of being examined by his own solicitor or counsel and of stating his case in public at the inquiry.
5. Any material witness he wishes called at the inquiry should, if reasonably practicable, be heard.
6. He should have the opportunity of testing by cross-examination conducted by his own solicitor or counsel any evidence which may affect him.

http://incentives.practicallaw.com/1-385-1407

Next steps for the investigation team

Once an interview has been concluded, the team should try and reflect, and debrief, before the next interview if there is time. However, often there is not.

Once all interviews have been concluded for that day, or group of days, the priority for the investigation team is to makes sure all interview notes are properly presented. This means

- good sentence structure; and
- no typos.

If there is, in the minds of the investigators, missing information then consideration can be given to posing a series of additional questions for the interviewee at the end of the interview notes. These should be clearly identified and the rationale for asking the question made clear. The question numbers may be indicated near to the section of the interview to which each question relates.

Interview notes should be sent back to interviewees within 5-7 working days of their interview. Investigators should also expect to receive them back as a validated record within a defined timeframe. This expectation should be made explicit to the interviewee at the end of the interview and also at the time the interview notes are sent to them.

Sending interviewees their interview record

There is no reason why this should not be accomplished electronically.
If the investigation team decides to provide an electronic copy to an interviewee then the following principles apply:

- The notes must be password protected with a password unique to the interviewee. A strong password contains letters, numbers, and punctuation marks. For example "sEpt3Mber".
- Make a record of the password and store it where it can be retrieved.
- Provide a set of instructions to the interviewee as to how to open their interview notes, what you want them to do with them, how they can make in text amendments, etc. Make sure the interviewee knows that if they do not return their notes within the timescales asked, they will receive only one reminder. Thereafter it will be assumed that they are satisfied with the content of their notes.
- Send the interview notes and password by separate emails, or via separate media.
- Always set up the email options so that you receive a delivery and a read receipt. This gives you an auditable trail, and highlights problems at an early stage.

3.2 What to do when you have completed all interviews and have all the interview notes returned as validated

Analysing interview notes can be challenging especially when they are voluminous.

A simple approach is as follows:

1. To take the terms of reference, in particular any critical questions posed, e.g. "Were the admission procedures carried out effectively?", and use these as themes against which data from the interviews is placed. Or, reflect as an investigation team and decide what the most important care management or case management concerns/problems were. For example: "There was a lack of effective risk assessments undertaken, including a complete lack of any relapse prevention planning and contingency planning", or: " The communication between the social workers, the school nurses and the health visitors was ineffective between 10 May and 25 August".

Deciding on what the care management concerns are

If the terms of reference for the investigation you are undertaking have provided the flexibility for you to identify the main care management concerns and have not presented you with any core questions to respond to in the investigation report, you do need a structured and auditable methodology for agreeing these with your subject/clinical/social care specialist advisers. One effective way of doing this is to use a consensus based approach.

- Each investigator and/or adviser (clinician, technical expert, social care professional) should, following his/her digestion of all the interview notes and any other relevant information including the chronology of events, identify what for him/her were the most important problems in the case. For example:
  - The management plan for patient X was inadequate and did not address XYZ needs.
  - There was a lack of effective communication and care planning between the community mental health team and the community alcohol team.
  - The GP who had seen child A on x occasions did not correctly diagnose the problem of X.
  - Patient A was prescribed a medication in spite of having made it explicit to staff that he/she had a life threatening allergy to this medication.
  - The community pharmacist dispensed double the prescribed amount of diazepam to the patient.
  - More than 50% of the health visitors' attempts to make contact with Child A and her family were unsuccessful. No effective action was subsequently taken to assess Child A.
  - The approach to the care management of the residents in residential home B was task orientated and not patient centred.

- Once each team member has identified what for him/her were the core problems, then these should be emailed to the lead investigator who can then assess the degree of agreement within the team. (The theory is if that you have all been involved in the same investigation there should be a high degree of agreement at this stage.) If there is little agreement then there will need to be a face-to-face or tele-conference so that the team can achieve unity on what the main care/case management problems were.

2. Once the investigation team has agreed the themes, questions or care/case management concerns (CMCs), against which it is going to analyse the information gathered, then the active analysis process can begin. The information to be analysed includes:
   - interview notes;
   - non-participant observers' findings/notes;
   - relevant parts of practice policies;
   - extracts from the case records/clinical records; and
   - photographs and schematics etc.

3. At Consequence UK we have found that the easiest and most accessible approach is for all investigation team members to have a copy of all interviews, single side printed.

It is helpful if the interview notes are uniquely identified in some way. For example each interviewee's notes are printed on coloured paper. E.g. Peter = pale blue, Jane = luminous pink. Alternatively if you go to "insert" on your computer toolbar, and choose shapes and then line, you can uniquely identify interview notes that way. For example Peter has double lines down the right hand margin of his notes, whereas Jane has dots and dashes.

It is also helpful if each set of interview notes is line referenced, that is every row has a number. If you are using Word 2007 go to "page layout", select "line numbers" and then "continuous".

Each investigator should read each interview record. If an interview took an hour, it will probably take approximately 30 minutes to read it properly. Therefore in terms of time management, if you interviewed for two days, then you need to allow a day each for reading all of the interview notes.

As you read segments that you know are relevant to the critical questions identified/TOR, or the themes agreed between you as a team, then you should cut this section of the interview transcript out, and place it with that theme/question/TOR If your interview extract goes with more than one theme or question, then cross reference. The least frustrating way to do this is to:

- copy out (i.e. rewrite or reprint) the relevant piece of the interview, printing as many as is required; or
- keep a cross referenced list and the print the additional extracts at the end, and place them accordingly; or
- do the analysis electronically.

4. You will in the process of doing this identify important information that does not particularly fit with the themes/questions identified for the "Findings" section of your investigation report. Cut these out too, and place them on a flip chart, or envelope labelled "other". You can do a straightforward thematic analysis on this data at the end using something like the National Patient Safety Agency's *Contributory Factors Framework.* (www.nrls.npsa.nhs.uk/resources/?entryid45=75605)

Visual example of interview extracts being placed against core themes

The photo above shows interview data (on the coloured paper) placed on the question/theme to which it best belongs (the white paper). This simple approach is called content analysis. Where data (information on the coloured paper) belongs with more than one question or theme, a cross referencing system can be used. This is made immeasurably easier if all interview notes are line referenced.

5. Once you have been through all of the interview notes, and assigned them as you believe is right, it is ideal if you then meet as a team and take each critical question/theme/CMC in turn and reflect on the data. Are you satisfied that the data belongs where you have placed it? During this process you may find that further subsets of data can be identified. For example if the critical question is:
   "Was the medication management of X reasonable? You may find that amongst the information you have placed against this question the following sub sets emerge:
   - type of medication and dosage;
   - monitoring and medication compliance;
   - management of side effects; and
   - decision to enable anti-psychotic depot to be administered by practice nurses at GP surgery.

If this happens it can assist in the formulation of a structured and logical investigation report.

The "fishbone" diagram (see Appendix 1) can also be used to enable themes from within discrete groups of data to emerge, however you may find it more meaningful to allow the data to speak for itself rather than forcing it into predefined categories that may or may not assist your analysis or the clarity of the investigation report.

6. Once all the data has been distributed and you have agreed as an investigation team that the data has been placed correctly you then need to decide what of the data constitutes contributory factors, and what data constitutes "root causes". You also need to map the contributory factors against the NPSA's or another human factor framework.

Identifying the contributory factors to care management concerns

Where the fishbone diagram is particularly helpful is where an investigation team needs to present the contributory factors to case management/care management failures (weaknesses or problems), and/or where the short answer to a critical question posed in the terms of reference is "no".
For example: "Was there an appropriate risk assessment, risk relapse plan and crisis plan for service user X?" If the answer to this is "no", then the investigation team should be able to present the contributory factors as to "why not?" The fishbone diagram incorporating the NPSA's *Contributory Factors Framework* can be very helpful in presenting the contributory factors analysis on a problem by problem basis.
Note: The NPSA's *Contributory Factors Framework* is a guide. It does not represent the totality of headings/themes for a contributory factors framework. For example in social care, mental health and learning disabilities the investigators will need to consider the following as contributory factor headings:

- interagency communications, with sub spines for each agency involved; and
- family involvement and dynamics.

The investigators may also want to use their own contributory factor headings. This is OK, however, it is recommended that you become familiar with the NPSA's framework first so that you have a solid understanding of how contributory factor frameworks should work.

If an investigator is interested in researching the field of contributory factor frameworks, then a simple Google search using the string "contributory factor frameworks" will yield reasonable results.

Challenges with contributory factor frameworks

One common challenge when using contributory factor frameworks is that investigation team members can find that individual pieces of data can fit with more than one contributory factor heading. This can be frustrating for the team.

In such circumstances, refer to the contributory factor framework included on in this book. The detail in it may enable you to resolve the problem. If not, then decide where the "best fit" is for the information and place it against that contributory factor. The usage of contributory factor frameworks in health and social care is qualitative rather than qualitative and investigators do need to bring a certain degree of common sense into the process.

Diagrammatic example of how you might approach the data analysis process

Note: The headings for the spines of the fishbone (see Appendix 1) may vary between the "management problems. However each organisation should have core headings that should be considered for the analysis of all care/case management concerns identified. These core headings should not prevent an investigator or investigation team from determining more appropriate headings where necessary.

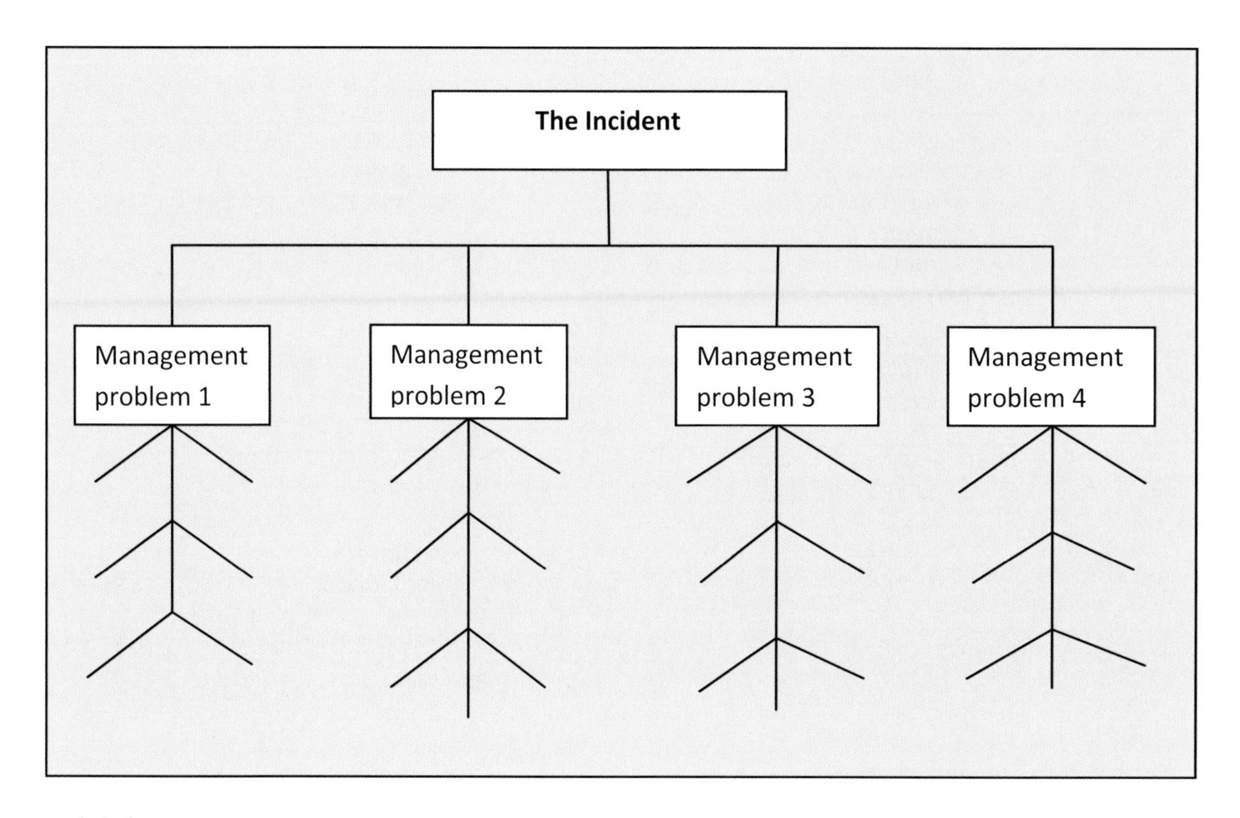

3.2.1 Worked example of care management concerns – the Avonside Review

The Avonside Review[7] was commissioned following a series of allegations of abuse of older people in an assessment unit in a mental health trust. The investigation was traumatic for the families of the "abused" and the staff. The abuse had been perpetrated by one person but the whole approach to the care and treatment of all residents was under scrutiny.

Overall the review found that the staff were committed to providing a good standard of care to the residents, however they had an outmoded approach and the unit was institutionalised.

The information gathering stage of the investigation was extensive with many interviews of staff and managers, as well as relatives of the abused. The information gathering stage also included the outputs from two half-day workshops where the critical success factors for the unit were explored with staff, and the systems and processes they had in place to deliver these.

The review team were committed to undertaking a structured approach to the information analysis and an approach which could be described and repeated by an independent assessor if necessary.

To achieve this the review team first mapped on a flip chart all of the problems and concerns it had identified. These were documented as each reviewer perceived them. Six flip charts were populated with this information.

The review team then grouped and themed these problems and concerns so that the core issues could be more succinctly defined. This exercise resulted in seven core problem statements.

[7] The Avonside Review, published April 2004, South Birmingham and Solihull NHS Trust

These were:

- the care regime was old fashioned;
- there had been a lack of consistent leadership (clinical and managerial);
- there were no embedded clinical governance structures;
- there had been ineffective operational management;
- the staff had lost their perspective of their core purpose;
- the staff were under developed; and
- the culture of the assessment unit was insular and inward looking.

The next step was to take all of the information contained in the interview records, etc, and to extract the information that helped the review team understand and articulate how and why the seven core problems existed. This was achieved by utilising the fishbone diagram and the NPSA's *Contributory Factors Framework*[8]. This activity highlighted to the review team that it had not distilled the core seven problem statements robustly enough. Four of the problem statements identified had almost exactly the same contributory factors. Consequently the review team amalgamated three of the original problem statements making the final number four. These were:

- there was a lack of consistent leadership (clinical and managerial);
- there were no embedded clinical governance structures in the unit;
- there had been ineffective operational management; and
- the staff had lost perspective of their core purpose.

The activity described above can be undertaken as a team event. However, for time efficiency there is merit in each member of an investigation team having undertaken their own brainstorming, grouping and theme development prior to a team meeting, and then the team can agree these via a telephone conference. This means that each team member can undertake structured analysis with the interview notes in preparation for the team meeting as described in 3.2 page 49.

[8] www.nrls.npsa.nhs.uk/resources/?entryid45=75605 - see *Contributory Factors Framework*

The investigation process

Step four:

Problem exploration: exploring the critical problems identified to isolate the most significant influencing factors

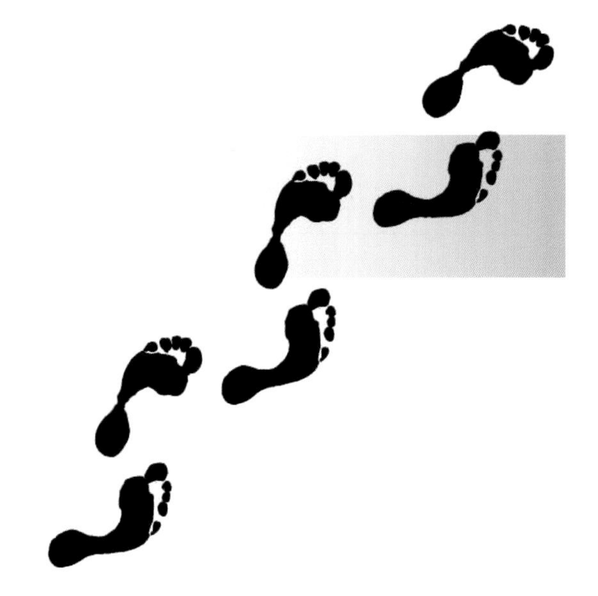

4.0 Introduction

Steps Three and Four are important steps in the investigation process. Unfortunately they are the least understood and remembered. Breaking down the analysis of the information collected into manageable chunks does aid the overall conduct of an investigation. It also aids the delivery of a logical, well structured investigation report.

Once the investigators have identified which information helps explain how and why the care management/case management problems occurred, it is time to agree the root causes for each case/care management concern (CMC).

Step Four requires the investigator to identify the root causes to each problem identified at Step Three. It is important that the root causes for each problem are identified on a problem by problem basis. To try and determine the root causes across all of the problems identified can lead investigators to lose their clarity of understanding as to what caused what. It is also important for investigators to remember that sometimes CMCs can be identified, the avoidance of which would not have prevented the incident from occurring. Classic examples of incidents where this can happen are:

- child abuse cases;
- poor outcomes of childbirth;
- homicide investigations involving mental health service users; and
- community suicides involving mental health service users.
- Older person abuse

In such cases it is doubly important that the contributory factor analysis and root cause identification process is undertaken on a CMC by CMC basis. It delivers a more honest and meaningful investigation process.

It is also important for investigators to accept that root causes can be repeated across the range of care/case management problems. If an investigation team does identify a common root cause, or root causes, all this means is that the recommendations made to address them need to be as robust as possible. It will also emphasise the priority of the recommendation.

4.1 What is a root cause?

A root cause is something that is deeply embedded in the systems and processes that should have been supporting the delivery of a safe and effective service, but has been identified as absent or not working as intended. It is something that, if remedied, should have a broad and sustainable impact on improving the safe and effective delivery of the service.

A root cause, therefore, will usually be related to:

- task design, policies and procedures;
- working conditions;
- education and training;
- communication systems, methods and pathways;
- organisational culture/departmental culture/team culture; and
- leadership and management arrangements.

Root causes are not usually related to:

- the acts and omissions of individual practitioners;
- the behaviour of a patient/client/service user; and
- family/carer dynamics and behaviours.

Where investigators find that an act or omission of a professional has been significant in allowing a problem to exist, it is preferable if this is described as a "proximal cause". That is, an act or omission occurring "near to" the problem occurrence. For example, if, in the opinion of the investigators, a significant cause of the staff not undertaking further risk assessments was because of their preconceptions of the service user as attention seeking, then they might say that "a proximal cause to the lack of risk assessment was the attitude of the professionals involved in his care and management".

4.2 Determining the root causes

If the contributory factor information has been arranged around a human factors framework (with or without the fishbone diagram), it may help the investigators to have clarity about what factors, in their opinion, had the most impact on the problem being considered. There is no magic formula for this, it is more that ordering the information using a human factors framework makes it easier to work with and assimilate information. It is not uncommon for the root causes to speak for themselves.

For example, a problem statement following the investigation of an attempted inpatient suicide might be: "There was insufficient attention paid to the risk profile of the service user. He had experienced a significant change in personal stressor but there was no repeat of his risk assessment between April and June."

There will be a range of data collected from interviews that will assist the investigators in understanding why there was insufficient attention paid to the service user's risk assessment.
It is likely that there will be information relating to:

- training and education;
- team leadership;
- staff perceptions about the service user;
- communications amongst the team; and
- task design i.e. the presence or absence of appropriate policies and procedures and the clarity of instruction within these, as well as the accessibility of these.

If the investigation reveals that there are no clinical guidelines on how and when a risk assessment should be undertaken, and staff have not received any training in risk assessment and relapse prevention, then one might reasonably say that:

- "the absence of up-to-date, accessible and understandable practice guidelines"; and
- "the lack of effective training in risk assessment and relapse prevention planning";

were the root causes.

A proximal cause would be something like "the staff in contact with the service user saw him as attention seeking and did not take seriously his behaviours or expressed concerns about himself. They had become desensitised to him".

Be aware

Investigators using the fishbone diagram can automatically assume that the fish "spine", or human factor heading with the most information attached to it must be a root cause. This is not always the case. It is important when determining the root cause or causes, that the investigators are mindful of the degree of the impact on the problem statement being analysed. One way of logically thinking this through is to ask oneself the following question:
"Recommendations must address root causes. If there was only one thing I could change on this fishbone to try and ensure this problem did not occur again what would it be?"
There may be two or three things you might like to address but you can only have one. What will it be? Where will maximum quality and safety improvement be achieved? Where will maximum preventability or risk reduction be achieved in relation to this problem?

Generally speaking there is usually more than one root cause to an identified problem. If as an investigator you were to elect to use the question posed above, it will be prudent to ask: "OK, we have identified the most important thing. What is the next most important issue that needs to be remedied to reduce the risk of problem recurrence?"

As a rough guide we suggest that this question should not be asked more than three times. This forces the investigator to really consider the overall importance and impact of a contributory factor, or a collection of contributory factors, on a problem.

Note: As already stated it is essential that this process is undertaken on a CMC by CMC basis. To try to look at the collected data en masse does not achieve clarity or focus in relation to root causes.

Furthermore, as stated in the introduction to this chapter, to look at the data en masse presupposes that the incident was preventable. This is not always the case. It is possible to identify clear and significant case/care management concerns which if removed would not guarantee the avoidance of the incident scenario, or have impacted on it in any significant way. The areas of health and social care where this can often happen are:

- mental health;
- learning disabilities;
- safeguarding children incidents; and
- safeguarding adults incidents.

In these areas it does transpire that even if everything had been done correctly, the incident being investigated may still have occurred and was not avoidable by virtue of different or better care or case management. These areas always have a range of variables that are outside of the control of the professionals providing care or case management.

Diagrammatic example of the association between the incident, care/case management concerns, contributory factors and root causes.

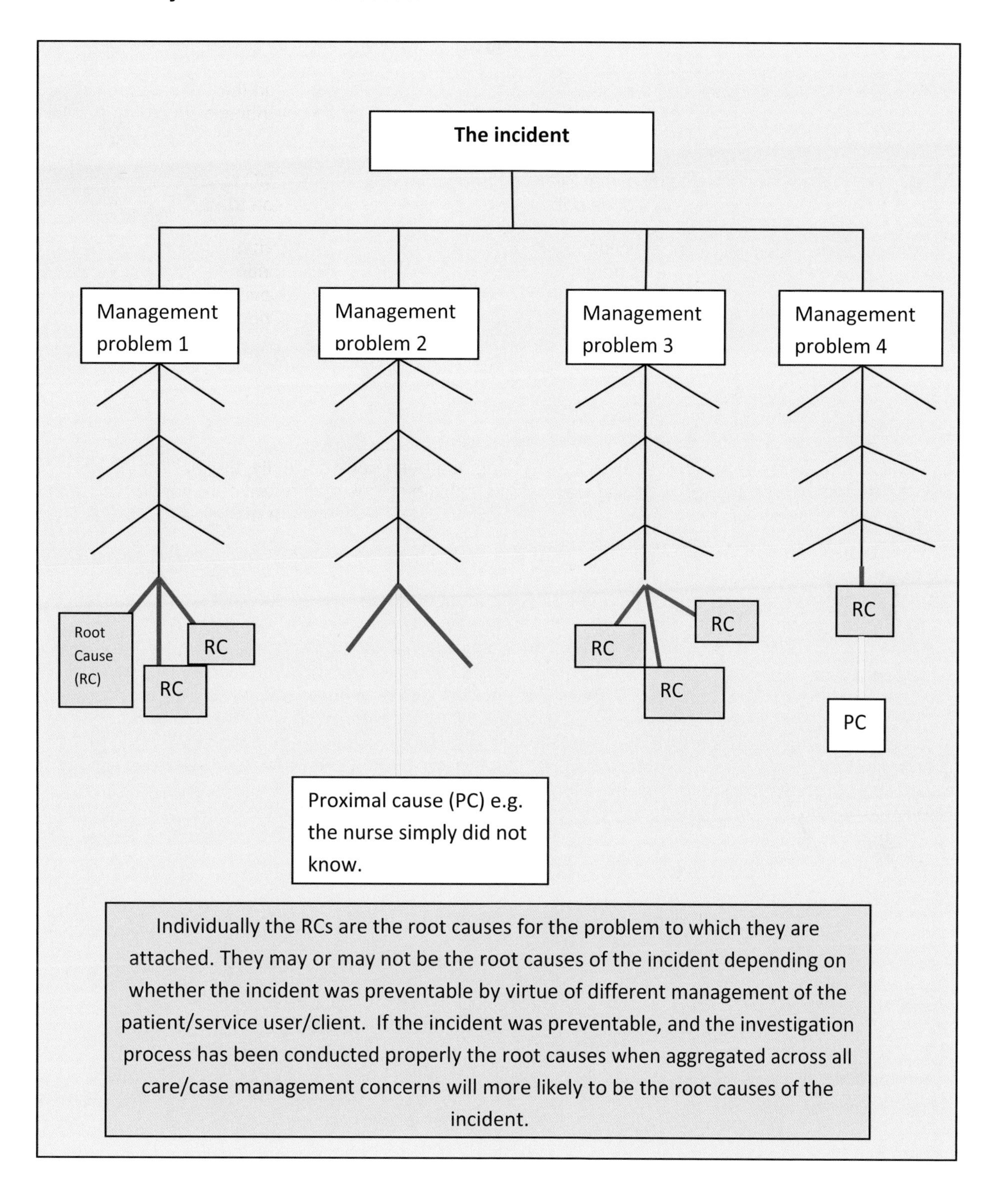

The investigation process

Step five:

Making recommendations

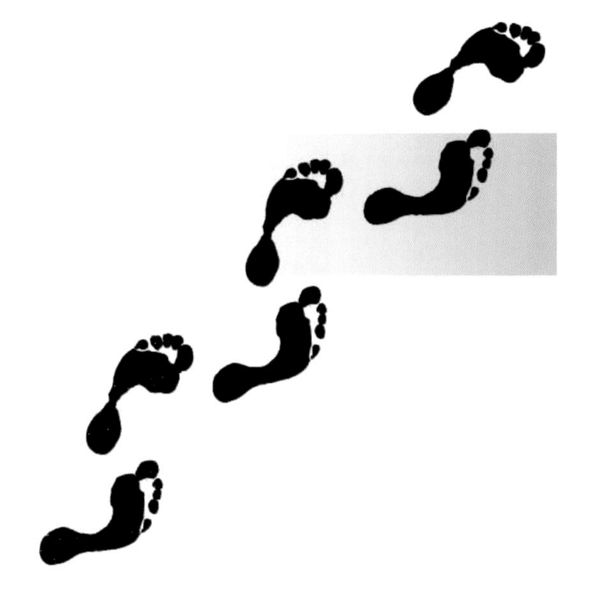

5.0 Introduction

Once an investigation team has reached agreement on the root causes of the identified care management/case management concerns, then recommendations can be considered and agreed.

A recommendation is an action the investigation team wants the commissioners of the investigation, and the involved services/team to consider. It is not the role of an investigation team to decide which recommendations will be accepted. Therefore it is not the role of an investigation team to devise the action plan. Action plans should be devised by those with the responsibility for making the agreed changes, and who therefore have the control and responsibility for seeing an action plan through. Currently in UK healthcare, internal investigation teams are often expected to generate action plans as an integral component of the investigation process. This is driven by the nationally determined timescales in which investigations must be completed, and commissioners of services expecting the delivery of the completed investigation reports, including the action plans, within these timescales. These drivers are resulting in action plans that are not properly formulated and do not always have buy in from the services expected to carry them forward.

One way of diminishing the negative impact of these drivers is for investigation teams to develop recommendations in partnership with the local services that need to implement them. This will result in recommendations that are more detailed and that set out the key features of any subsequent action implementation plan.

It is important for all commissioners of investigation to remember that until agreed/accepted recommendations of an investigation have been implemented, and the impact of implementation has been determined, the investigation process is not complete. If one accepts that the purpose of undertaking an investigation is to improve practice, systems and processes it is difficult not to agree with this. Consequently, although implementation of recommendations can only come after the investigation report has been accepted, implementation is also addressed in this chapter for ease of reference.

5.1 Key features of effective recommendations

How an investigation team designs and presents the recommendations is as important as how the active phases of the investigation are conducted.

Recommendations need to make explicit what is required, and the rationale for making the recommendation.

Investigator(s) also need to be aware of the reliability characteristics of different types of recommendation. These characteristics indicate whether, when implemented, the recommendation will have any sustainability as regards changing practice or quality improvement. These characteristics are:

- physical interventions;
- interventions utilising distance, time and place;
- human action interventions; and
- administrative interventions.

Physical interventions
Generally speaking these are interventions that design out, as far as possible, the opportunities for error to occur. Consequently this type of intervention can involve the designing out of the human component in the process.
Health examples of this are:
- The management of blood banks, which are predominantly computerised.
- Automatic blood gas analysers where the results are automatically printed.
- Modern anaesthetic machines with fittings that do not allow them to be set up the wrong way.

Non-health examples are:
- A modern underground rail system where the platforms are lined with non-breakable doors, which do not open until the incoming train has come to a standstill with its doors aligned to the platform doors.

Time, distance and placement interventions
These interventions largely speak for themselves. Examples of such interventions are:
- the removal of potassium from inpatient wards;
- the preparation of chemotherapy medicines in specifically designated areas;
- offsite storage of medical records with specialist companies, using barcode technology;
- putting all oral penicillin-containing antibiotics in a ward's clinical treatment room in a designated brightly coloured box, clearly labelled " everything in this box contains penicillin"; and
- time pause interventions prior to the start of invasive treatments, where all professionals present double check that they have the right patient, that they are doing the right operation/treatment, and, that it is on the right side of the patient/right body part.

A non-health example is:
- the automatic closure of train doors 45 seconds prior to train departure.

Human action interventions
These are interventions that rely on changing the behaviour of humans. An example of a human action intervention is:
- telling or reminding staff to undertake a task in a prescribed way.

Any recommendation that is specifically targeted how people behave is generally a human action intervention.

Administrative interventions
These are interventions that target systems and processes such as:
- policies and procedures, their content, accessibility and readability;
- the content and frequency of training programmes;
- how stock is ordered; and
- communication systems and pathways that rely on human execution.

5.1.1 The value of the different intervention types
All of the intervention types have merit; however, some are more accessible than others to local organisations, regional and national bodies.

Physical interventions by their nature will tend to require considerable research investment and therefore require development on a national or international basis. This investment is necessary to generate safety solutions that design out our capacity as humans to make mistakes. Consequently physical interventions are not often accessible to local organisations.

Natural (time/distance), human and administrative interventions however are much more accessible to local organisations and health and social care communities.

What local organisations must accept however is that "high reliability" is rarely achievable with interventions that rely on people performing consistently, and doing what they should.
This means that organisations must pay close attention to the detail of the implementation plans for any administrative, human action and natural intervention recommended. It is the detail of the implementation plan that can enhance reliability and ensure that any improvements made are more robust and enduring.

5.1.2 SMART recommendations

Recommendations also need to be SMART, that is:

- specific; straightforward;
- measurable; meaningful;
- achievable; agreed upon, attainable; action orientated;
- realistic; relevant; results orientated; and
- timely; trackable; targeted.

Designing recommendations that meet SMART criteria is essential. Recommendations that meet these criteria are more likely to be accurately interpreted by those receiving the investigation report. Consequently the implementation plans agreed are more likely to have multiple points of measurement. This in itself is important if an organisation is to be able to demonstrate the impact of implementation. An example of a recommendation that does not meet SMART criteria is:
"All staff must be reminded to follow the nursing observation policy."

This recommendation could be worded differently, for example as follows:
"Nursing observation practice in in-patient areas needs to evidence that it complies with the organisation's observation policy".

The recommendation could then be spelt out in more detail as follows:

- "Team leaders need to conduct periodic non-participant observation studies of how their teams conduct their day to day duties, including the observation of service users on timed observations.
  - Team members need to become engaged in the non-participant observer activity so that they properly appreciate how they and their colleagues are going about their core activities.
  - The non-participant observation periods need to be for no more than an hour at a time, and for multiple periods over the course of a defined period of time, so that staff become used to the activity and are therefore less likely to change their normal patterns of behaviour.
  - The observations must be recorded and fed back to the staff at the end of the activity.
- Team leaders must audit the means by which the nursing staff and support workers record the observations undertaken of a service user, to ensure that staff notate the quality of their interaction with a service user, and their impression of mood.
- Team managers' supervision must include reflection on how they monitor staff compliance with core clinical standards such as nursing observation practice.
- Each team manager will be expected to include a section on nursing observation practice in his/her twice yearly governance activity report."

The recommendation is immediately more measurable, and much more likely to impact on practice. Simply telling people what they should do without any practice framework or idea for achieving this, or evidencing it, is unlikely to result in the positive changes in practice that are required. Neither do such recommendations result in sustainable quality improvement.

5.2 Designing a recommendation

When thinking of how to articulate a recommendation an investigator/investigation team first needs to be clear about what the recommendation is to achieve. For example if the purpose of making a recommendation is to achieve an overall improvement in medicines administration practice, making a recommendation that says:

"All staff need to be reminded to adhere to the medicines administration policy" is unlikely to achieve this.

The investigators need to think through, with appropriate specialist input/advice, what activities need to be undertaken to improve compliance with the principles of the medicines administration policy. Then the recommendation can have a "headline" with the detail of what is required set below this. The example detailed above gives an idea of how this can be formulated.

When making recommendations the investigation team must give due consideration to:

- To whom, or to which committee, the recommendation is directed. Is it a recommendation for the team involved in the incident? Is it a recommendation that has applicability across a service? Is it a recommendation that has applicability organisation wide?
  If it is a recommendation primarily for the local team, then this should be made explicit.
  If it is a recommendation for a corporate committee or individual, this should be made explicit.
- The priority of the recommendation. Is it something that is safety critical and needs to be addressed with urgency? Is it something that needs to be actioned but there is time to look at how

the recommendation sits alongside other streams of quality and safety improvement activities already underway?

The example recommendations on the following pages represent ways of setting out recommendations that can then easily be translated into an action plan.

Example 1: Template for presenting a summary of the recommendations made[9]

Critical care delivery or service problem e.g. Rigidity in practice and care regime			
Root Causes	1. Isolated care environment 2. Autocratic local and service management culture 3. No active service clinical governance or clinical improvement programme 4. No investment in the skills and knowledge development of staff		
Recommendations	Type/nature of recommendation	Priority	Targeted at
1. Undertake a review of all isolated care environments to ascertain current models of care, styles of management and the competencies of staff	Administrative	High – safety critical	Governance Committee of the Board
2. Identify the core competencies that staff in this environment should possess by grade and job role, and undertake a training needs analysis and development plan to enable staff to achieve and practise to the desired competencies	Administrative	High – staff must know what they are doing – safety critical	HR department with Service Management Team
3. Review the personal development plans for the local and service managers and support them in participating in a 360° assessment process, with subsequent attached development programmes, to identify current and future development needs	Administrative	Medium – desirable. Not safety critical as there are other systems and processes in place for assessing management effectiveness	HR, Directorate/Service Lead & Clinical Director
4. Commission the clinical governance department to develop a clinical governance/improvement work programme with the service management team and members of each team	Administrative	Medium – high. This recommendation cannot take place before recommendation 2, and ideally 3, have been achieved	Governance Committee of the Board in partnership with Directorate / Service Management Team* (see note)

---

[9] Dineen, M (2004) "Reliability in quality and safety improvement strategies", *Health Care Risk Report*, vol 10, issue 5 (April 2004), pages 12 – 15.

Example 2: How a recommendation could be presented in an investigation report
Recommendation:
The Managing Director at the St Winifred's Group Nursing Homes needs to develop a clear education strategy for its staff.

Although the investigation team identified clear evidence of staff attending educational seminars relevant to the care required by the residents, the overall approach to the training programme was incoordinate and not prioritised. There was no clear strategy to ensure that staff had the core skills to deliver their tasks and responsibilities effectively and safely.

Priority level and timeliness for implementation
This recommendation is important; however, the Review Team recognises that it requires a substantial amount of work. Consequently the Review Team suggests that within two months of the acceptance of this report, St Winifred's Group presents the commissioning PCT and the Local Authority with its action plan for progressing this recommendation and its proposed timescales for implementation.

The Review Team suggests that this recommendation should have been fully implemented within 12 months of the acceptance of this report.

Components of the recommendation
In taking this recommendation forward, the Review Team suggests that:

1. A clear map is made of the specific skills that staff (qualified and/or unqualified) need, to deliver the expected standard of care to residents. It is expected that this map will contain at least the following.

   Core skills for the Band 7s, to achieve the desirable model and standards of care, include:
   - Leadership skills e.g. facilitating teams, appraisals, performance management, reflective case reviews, complaints management, incident management/learning from experience, budget awareness, off-duty planning and project management skills.
   - All Band 7s must have undertaken a specialist older persons course to diploma level or equivalent.

   Extended core skills for all qualified nurses should include:
   - dysphagia training;
   - assessment of dysphagia (a core number of staff need this, so that the skills are available on each unit);
   - mental health awareness;
   - continence management; and
   - tissue viability.

   All healthcare attendants need to be achieving the following basic competencies:
   - assisting with personal hygiene;
   - oral hygiene;
   - foot care;
   - nutritional awareness;
   - safer handling techniques;
   - assisting with feeding, ensuring adequate fluid intake;
   - communication skills; and
   - sensory impairment awareness.

   Extended competencies for the healthcare attendants could include:
   - PEG feeds (setting up, monitoring);
   - nutritional screening;
   - clinical observations including BP, P, RR and temperature (and blood glucose); and
   - record keeping, i.e. making their own independent record of care delivered in the resident's progress notes.

2. All qualified and unqualified staff are asked to self assess themselves against the skills map. It is essential that staff understand that honesty about personal skill development requirements is pivotal to the success of the final training plan.

3. St Winifred's Group gives consideration to the spread of enhanced skills and competencies that need to be available in its nursing homes, on a shift by shift basis. This will help gauge the numbers of staff who need investment in their skill and knowledge development in the short term i.e. the next 12 to 18 months.

4. St Winifred's Group could consider developing a journal club where individual or small groups of staff can take responsibility for researching specific aspects of older persons' care and preparing a briefing summary or presentation for colleagues. It is essential that all grades of staff, including healthcare attendant staff, are included in this activity. Furthermore, all Band 6s should be expected to take the lead for the preparation of at least one topic per 18 month period.

Target audience
This recommendation needs to be considered by the local managers for each of the St Winifred's Group Nursing Homes, ideally at their monthly management meeting.

The recommendation also needs to be considered by the senior management team and Managing Director for the St Winifred's Group Nursing Homes.

Case study contributed by Louise Dawes, Modern Matron, Community for Sandwell Mental Health NHS and Social Care Trust (2004)

Background
In October 2003 an elderly patient sustained a fall in an inpatient unit. The patient sustained a significant laceration to the head requiring 14 sutures in a nearby A&E department. Louise was commissioned to review the circumstances of the fall and the patients care pathway. This was undertaken using the investigative framework detailed in *Six steps to root cause analysis* (Dineen 2002).
The following excerpts from the subsequent incident review report have been contributed by Louise, to help demonstrate the pivotal place of the human factors analysis (causal analysis), and achieving clarity about the root causes.

Excerpts from human factors analysis

Factor	Positive aspects	Negative aspects
Team	Team members know who to contact for help Team was able to identify the seriousness of the incident Team openness New Ward Manager two weeks previously	Previous managerial and clinical leadership has not been effective Staff are unsure of their role in crisis situation Delegation of tasks not reflective of skill mix Staff did not follow advice/directions immediately Team are not regularly supported by medical staff Team staffing does not reflect the patients' present needs

Factor	Positive aspects	Negative aspects
Communication	Nursing records are easy to read and follow the policy in respect of style of presentation Records are stored together Clear verbal communication between CN, SN and SG Right people contacted at correct time Multidisciplinary reviews are held regularly by the team	CIRA forms are completed but not followed up i.e. not seen by doctors On occasions entries are not made in the nursing notes for several days (outside the Trust's policy guidelines for continuing care environments) Request for help from CN or SG could have been made by HC1 or HC2 Care plans not reviewed as planned or altered accordingly Doctors not informed about falls/injuries beyond the doctors' book

Factor	Positive aspects	Negative aspects
Task	CIRA forms completed Generalised risk assessment form used CPA forms utilised Modern matron available for specialist advice Observation policy Weight chart completed	Appropriate forms used but not always completed appropriately CIRA procedure not fully followed – no Dr review, no observation following being found on the floor No falls risk and care plans were utilised Blood glucose monitoring forms not utilised No benchmark/protocol/ procedures in respect of physical procedures Outdated care plans No specialist assessment or paperwork relevant to this patient group Blood results are not always considered Risk assessment – vulnerable adult section not completed Records of observation not completed according to policy

Excerpts from recommendations made - 23 in total

Risk elements

1 Risk assessment forms should be fully completed including the vulnerable adult section.
2 That a full risk assessment is completed on admission to a continuing care ward, taking into account physical health needs that could impact on the mental state of the individual.
3 That specialised assessment life histories are devised for continuing care wards and completed during the first four weeks on the wards.

Patient care elements

1 That all patients' physical state is monitored throughout their hospital stay involving monitoring and reviewing by the multidisciplinary team involving medical staff.
2 That clinical protocols/benchmarks are created to ensure physical monitoring is correctly carried out, i.e. fluid balance monitoring, blood glucose monitoring to decrease the impact of dehydration etc, and the mental wellbeing of the individual is thus maximised.
3 Specific patient care plans be developed and reviewed according to evidence-based practices.
4 Following a fall of unknown cause, basic observations will be made.

5 The medical staff should be kept informed about the falls a patient has.
6. Nursing notes must be maintained according to the trust procedures in respect of frequency of entries (policy number 12.6, p.5, section 4.0).

Nursing management elements

1 The ward skill mix is considered and reviewed taking into account care practice and patient changes on a regular basis.
2 Mandatory training to be provided about the importance of monitoring physical health problems and how to carry this out.
3 When managing the rota, the manager should ensure that the skill levels of each shift are reasonably equal to ensure that a consistency of care and knowledge is always available.
4 Nursing staff will fully implement the observation policy, including the use of the observation report form.

General elements

1 Fire extinguishers should not be located sticking out on corridor walls, but placed in places that make passing them easy but accessible.
2 The purchase of up to date written resources to support physical care practices for example, the Royal Marsden Hospital manual of clinical nursing procedures.
3 Trained first aiders should be available on each ward.
4 The development of the electronic communication of diagnostic investigatory results.
5 The development of a younger onset dementia service.

Constructive comment

One of the challenges experienced by Louise was the volume of recommendations she made following this RCA review. Whilst she had separated them out in terms of type, Louise felt that 23 recommendations was overwhelming and that she would have liked to have evolved a more concise and targeted list of recommendations. She was dubious as to the recommendations that would be taken forward to full implementation, and also was under confident with regard to the impact the recommendations would have in sustainable quality and safety improvement.
The author and Louise jointly reviewed the original human factors analysis undertaken to ascertain whether it was possible to achieve the degree of focus Louise aspired to. The observations we made were as follows:

- The human factors analysis was very broad and thorough. The author particularly liked the way in which Louise had identified both positive and negative aspects about the case management.
- The analysis was not linked to any particular care management concern/problem. Doing this may have assisted Louise in targeting her final recommendations. It may have also enabled her to be quite clear about the root causes of the specific problems she had identified.
- There was no identification of the overall root causes. Louise had stopped her analysis at the level of identifying contributory factors. Consequently the author and Louise revisited the human factors analysis, and distilled the following fundamental causes from this:
    - ineffective managerial leadership;
    - ineffective clinical leadership;
    - inconsistency in the support provided by the medical team; and
    - lack of quality monitoring and feedback in respect of essential clinical care and safety orientated policies and procedures.

Louise's recommendations, therefore, needed to target these four things specifically. Unless these four root causes are effectively addressed, then the core problems she identified in her investigation are more likely to continue.

5.3 Responsibilities of those receiving recommendations

Recommendations are just that. They are things to be considered as worthwhile doing. However, there is no obligation to act on a recommendation. There is however an obligation to give it due and careful consideration, weighing up the potential benefits of implementation and the risks of non-implementation. If a decision is made not to accept a recommendation there should be a clear and rational explanation as to why.

It is therefore the duty of those commissioning serious incident investigations to:

- Assess the risk of non-action on the recommendation, i.e. living with the status quo.
- Explore the range of options available to meet the principles of the recommendation if the recommendation is accepted for implementation.
- Assign appropriate people, time and financial resource to implement any action plan agreed to implement the recommendation.

- Ensure that implementation of the recommendation is auditable.
- Undertake a failsafe analysis of the agreed action plan to ensure that it is as robust and reliable as possible.
- Ensure that there is an agreed methodology and agreed timescales for measuring the impact of the recommendation in the short, medium and longer term.
- Ensure that any significant resource requirements are integral to the annual business plan.

Of the above, the weighing up of benefit is an essential step, and no recommendation should simply be accepted without the potential benefits of implementation versus the risks of non-implementation being considered. Everyone in health and social care is busy, and it is too easy to say "yes we'll do that" without proper consideration. Commissioners of serious incident investigations must remember that investigators base recommendations on the outputs of their investigation, and may not be aware of existing quality and safety improvement activities in the service to which a recommendation is targeted.

In the acceptance, rejection, absorption into an existing project, or sidelining of a recommendation, persons involved in this decision must make sure they are aware of the existing and planned activities so that right decisions can be made.

Whatever approach a health or social care organisation takes to considering recommendations and devising action plans, the style of action plan depicted below is not appropriate. It lacks detail, rigour and measurability.

Example of an action plan that lacks necessary detail

No	Title	Risk Rating	Lead Professional	Review Date	Target for completion
1	Undertake a review of all isolated care environments to ascertain current models of care, styles of management and the competencies of staff	High	Director of Nursing	3 months	12 months
2	Identify the core competencies that staff in this environment should possess by grade and job role, and undertake a training needs analysis and development plan to enable staff to achieve and practise to the desired competencies	High	Director of Nursing	6 months	6 months
3	Review the personal development plans for the local and service managers and support them in participating in a 360° assessment process, with subsequent attached development programmes, to identify current and future development needs	Medium	Head of the Directorate for 'Y'	12 months	18 months

The above table is not untypical of action plans found in some NHS trusts; however it is not an action plan, it is a summary of the headlines of an action plan. Action plans should have the same good practice criteria as recommendations. They should be SMART. To achieve this they should set out in detail how the recommendation is going to be taken forward and identify the specific components of the plan. Doing this in line with accepted project management principles would enable a more robust action plan to be developed. The following are core features of a robust action plan:

- The key individuals from whom input is required would be clearly identified and recorded.
- The key activities required to achieve "a review of all isolated care environments" would be identified and recorded.
- The range of models of care would be mapped, and the requirement for an affinity and gap analysis made explicit.
- The time scales for each discrete component of the action plan would be agreed, recorded and

monitored.

- The resources required for the implementation of the plan would be scoped, agreed, provided and recorded.
- The sponsor for the action plan would be identified and recorded.
- Review dates would be agreed and recorded.
- Overall accountability for the delivery of the action plan would be agreed and recorded.

In addition to the above, it is good practice to conduct an option appraisal, especially where there are significant cost implications in the implementation of the recommendation.

An action plan meeting the key features mentioned above might look something like the example presented below.

Author's comment
If health and social care organisations consistently developed more detailed and measurable action plans then it would, when required, be far easier for them to produce the evidence for the actions they have taken when asked by external assessment bodies to do so. It is my experience that when organisations are asked for evidence of implementation, and also evidence of an impact assessment, they can struggle to produce this. If all relevant data is appended to the incident file stored on an organisation's risk management or incident management database, requests for evidence of change may be more easily produced.

Author's recommendation
Commissioners of investigations may wish to utilise the revised action planning templates produced by the National Patient Safety Agency (NPSA). These include prompts for option appraisal and impact appraisal during the action planning process. The templates can be located via the National Reporting and Learning Service area of the NPSA website under "resources". The following link was active at the time of writing this publication: http://www.nrls.npsa.nhs.uk/resources/?entryid45=59847

Example – A measurable action plan

Title	Undertake a review of all isolated care environments to ascertain current models of care, styles of management and the competencies of staff				
Project Sponsor	Director of Quality and Innovation				
Project Lead	Head of Governance				
Project Team	Modern Matron for X	Governance facilitator X	Governance facilitator Y	Specialist Nurse Z	Clinical Lead P
Resources Required - Time	X days for the project lead	X days for the project team members			
Resources Required – financial resource	This project requires minimal financial resource.	Resources required: ▪ Estimated travel costs ▪ Estimated admin support costs ▪ Estimated subsistence costs ▪ Laptop Input from the clinical audit and governance support team			
Core Activities for project delivery	1. Identify the range/ number of isolated teams/care environments, and create a map of these	2. Scope the spread of specialisms working remotely, e.g. learning disabilities	3. Collate, from the service management teams, their current approach to ensuring that remote teams comply with local and corporate policies and are fully integrated into the service's governance arrangements	4. Undertake a sample of site visits, to: - conduct interviews with a sample of staff across the grade spectrum - conduct non-participant observer studies - observe team meetings	5. To facilitate a series of workshops with staff working in the identified care environments to find out from them how they perceive: - their education and training needs - integration with the wider services - effectiveness of local managers. The outputs from each workshop will be recorded.
Timescales for the delivery of the core plan	6 weeks from commencing project	6 weeks from commencing project	6 weeks from commencing project	Complete within 3 months	Complete within four months
Core Output from the Project to be delivered within 7 months	The findings of this project will be detailed in a report for submission to the organisation's governance and risk committee. It will detail what essential work needs to be undertaken by each local service to ensure that its isolated teams and care environments are meeting local and national standards, as well as being fully integrated with the service's established governance systems and processes.				

The investigation process

Step six:

The investigation report

6.0 Introduction

The investigation report sets out the findings, conclusions and recommendations of the investigation team or investigator. It needs to set these out;

- logically;
- succinctly; and
- in a format that is accessible to a varied readership. This may include professionals and lay people, non-executive directors of your organisation, the patient/client and families/carers.

There are a plethora of texts on effective report writing and this chapter does not aim to repeat the very good information contained within them. This chapter is dedicated to the presentation of an effective investigation report, following the investigation of a serious incident in health or social care.. The content of this chapter is influenced by the personal and professional development of the author.

The author is confident that at the time of writing (2011) the principles espoused meet with all current national guidance provided to health and social care professionals, in relation to investigation reports of serious untoward incidents including safeguarding incidents.

6.1 Writing the report

The most important thing for an investigation team to remember is that the quality of content will be directly affected by the quality of the investigation undertaken. It does not matter how well one can write. If there has been insufficient investigation and a lack of rigour in how the information gathered during an investigation has been analysed, the quality of the investigation report will be adversely affected.

The second most important thing for an investigation team to remember is that a good investigation methodology, and a clear, structured and repeatable approach as to how the information gathered was analysed, will help in the delivery of an investigation report that;

- is logical;
- has clarity; and
- makes the evidence base for its findings and conclusions explicit.

These characteristics are essential components of the effective investigation report.

6.1.1 First things first

A report template

Make sure you have an investigation report template that you can use. It takes a huge amount of stress out of getting started with the writing of it.

Most NHS organisations should have report writing templates that comply with the principles promoted by the National Patient Safety Agency in August 2010 in its Root Cause Analysis (RCA) investigation report writing templates[10]. However, it is the author's perspective that there are some elements of the templates that will not deliver the requirements of an effective investigation report, especially if in the interests of being open, the report is to be made available to the patient/service user/client and relevant family members and/or carers. The author therefore encourages readers of *Six steps* to reflect on the NPSA requirements and to think through how best those requirements can be delivered, without compromising the readability and purpose of the investigation report. Families want to know:

- what happened (the chronology);
- how it happened (the important care delivery and service delivery lapses);
- why it happened (the contributory factors and root causes to each identified care delivery and service delivery lapse);
- where care and/or service delivery met, or exceeded, local and national expectations;
- conclusions in relation to predictability and preventability; and
- recommendations to address to identified root causes.

In addition to the above points it is central to health and social care investigation reports that they set out to what extent the patient/service user/client and his or her family/carers have been involved by the investigation team. In the case of a mental health homicide, the report should also set out what efforts were made to contact the family of the victim (most easily achieved via victim support or the family liaison officer service provided by the local constabulary, if the victim's family is not already known to mental health services).

A good report template should lead the report's author through their report writing experience and ensure that all elements are covered.

A style sheet

Agreeing a style sheet for investigation reports is a useful tool for;

- reducing the stress one can experience;
- ensuring that the report has a consistent style throughout in relation to:
  - type face style;
  - chapter headings;
  - sub-headings;
  - section numbering;
  - main bullet point and sub bullet point style;
  - margin widths;
  - how quotations are presented; and
  - how references to publications are made.

The executive summary

The executive summary can be challenging to write and opinion varies as to whether it should be done before trying to write the main body (findings) section of the report, or once the main body and conclusions etc have been completed. The author of this book considers it very much depends on one's own writing style and can often be influenced by the complexity of the investigation undertaken. Generally speaking if there is clarity on the overall conclusions of the investigation team, then the executive summary is relatively easy to write.

---

[10] http://www.nrls.npsa.nhs.uk/resources/?EntryId45=75419

6.1.2 Challenges in report writing

Should the report have one or more authors?

All members of the investigation team should contribute to the final content of the investigation report. However, it is generally better for the report to be written by one team member, rather than multiple team members writing different elements of a report. Different authors generally mean more than one writing style which can adversely affect the flow of a report.

Our findings are not complimentary of the care and treatment provided to the patient/client/ service user

If you are going to criticise the care or case management you need to ensure that your evidence base for doing so is robust. If it is simply your opinion as a team that the care/case management was not very good, that is not a very strong evidence base. However if you have used the principles of the substitution test as set out in the National Patient Safety Agency's *Incident decision tree*, and have therefore asked a wider group of professionals working in the professional field about approaches to care/case management in similar circumstances, and their perspectives reflect those of the investigation team, then the evidence base for making a criticism is much stronger.

What about use of language? Is it OK to use words such as 'failure', 'poor', 'duty of care'?

Use of language is very important in an investigation report. It is important that it is written unemotionally. By this the author means avoiding the use of emotionally laden language.

The following shows how this can be achieved:

"Nurse A failed to check the drugs properly against the medicines chart."

would be better expressed as:

"Nurse A did not following the steps described in the hospital drug administration policy when checking the medicines for B. The specific steps omitted were: .... The nurses involved told the investigation that the reason these steps were not undertaken was because:

- ...."

The alternative wording achieves much more than the first sentence. It:

- is more measured and professional;
- states the facts; and
- tells the reader of the report precisely what aspects of practice were not delivered as one might have expected.

Furthermore the sentence is not open to misinterpretation. It leaves nothing to chance.

Another example is:

"The health visitors attempted to make contact with the mother of Baby Y on 10 occasions. They were only successful on three of these. Their actions following the failed home visits were inadequate."

An alternative could be:

"The health visitors attended at the home of Baby Y, on the following dates:

- date 1
- date 2
- date 3 etc

There were a total of 10 home visits, however, the health visitors only elicited a response from the occupants of Baby Y's home on the:

- date 1
- date 2
- date 3

In such circumstances the local operation policy (insert name of policy and date) requires that a health visitor undertakes the following activities:

- activity 1
- activity 2
- activity 3

The investigation team have found no evidence via documentation review, or during interviews with the health visitors, that these activities were undertaken until after the X date. It is the perspective of the investigation team that the health visitors should have acted after Y date. .....The health visitors involved told the investigation team that their reasons for not acting sooner were:

- ...."

Although the alternative wording here is longer than the first sentence, better, more accurate and balanced information would be conveyed. It is a misperception that a good investigation report is a short report. A good investigation report is one that sets out the facts and the evidence to support what the author(s) of a report are saying, in an easy to digest format but also in sufficient depth so that what happened and why can be properly understood.

The reader of an investigation report should not be left wondering what the evidence base is for anything written in the findings section of a report. Neither should they find themselves on an emotional roller coaster.

Using names of staff, the patient etc in the report

It is preferable if before writing the report, the report's author devises codes for all persons who would otherwise need to be named. There is no need to name staff in an investigation report. The purpose of the investigation report is to communicate the findings of the investigation team and its recommendations. Clearly identifiable individuals within the report can detract from this. Where staff are named it is easy for a reader of your report to get caught up with the 'person' or personality rather than reading the findings.

In de-identifying the report document, authors also need to be mindful of the use of locality names, and places. For example "the service user was an asylum seeker from Uganda whose MP was supporting their application to be in the UK" may make the service user identifiable. Similarly referring to the hospital, GP surgery etc by name will increase the opportunity of staff involved to be identified. This is not to say that place and location names should not be used but that the authors of investigation reports need to be mindful of the implications of doing so.

Another reason for ensuring that there is no breach of individuals' identities is where requests are made for release of the report under the Freedom of Information Act.

Authors of investigation reports must be aware that although a report may be de-identified this will not always protect the anonymity of staff or the patient/client/family. In very small communities if the incident was of significance, a broad range of people may know who was involved. There is nothing you can do about this. There will always be limitations to the extent to which individuals' identities can be protected.

Delivering a report that does the investigation justice

This is a challenge. Ensuring that the investigation does evidence a robust and effective investigation is a skill in its own right. It is a skill, as with many skills, that evolves with practice. There are however a number of things that can assist an investigation team in delivering a report that properly represents the quality of their investigation:

- using a proof reader to ensure that there are no grammatical errors in the report, and to highlight where it lacks clarity and there is weakness in the presentation of evidence base;
- having the report checked for consistency in style and formatting; and
- involving a third party at the data analysis stage of the investigation. An insightful, but uninvolved other, can enable an investigation team to identify any important information/evidence gaps at the data analysis stage when the situation can be remedied reasonably easily.

Lack of time

The author has no magical solutions to this challenge. However, if at all possible, make time in your diary for report writing and try and ensure that you can conduct this in an environment where you will not be disturbed. It is the author's experience that writing investigation reports always takes much longer than one anticipates, but that setting aside uninterrupted time makes the process easier.

Version control

Version control is essential. Each new draft, or partly completed draft should be rigorously version controlled. Using a simple referencing system such as XYZ *Draft report V1.0* etc is quite sufficient to achieve this.

Investigators may also wish to watermark the document as "draft". The watermark facility on a computer is commonly found under "page layout" and is clearly identified.

Investigators may also consider notating the report title and version number in the footer of each version of the report created.

Ensuring that all key interviewees and stakeholders have the opportunity to review and comment on the penultimate draft before content is finalised

It is essential that key interviewees have the opportunity to comment on the draft investigation report before it is finalised. There are a number of reasons for this:

- it is common courtesy;
- if professionals are criticised then they have the right to read the evidence base on which they are criticised and to challenge this if insufficient;
- key professionals who have given evidence/information to the investigators should be enabled to comment on the use of language and expression in the investigation report; and
- it is a useful way of engaging professionals in the report's conclusions and also in seeking feedback about the recommendations.

If family members and patients/service users/clients have contributed to the report's content, then the sections they have directly influenced should be made available to them in draft, so that they can confirm that they are satisfied with how the investigation team has presented the information. It is best if this is accomplished by providing a supervised reading opportunity.

Other stakeholders
This includes the commissioners for the investigation and other interested parties such as the director of a service, the clinical lead for a service, team managers etc.

Depending on the report content and conclusions, consideration should be given to seeking the perspective of the organisation's legal advisors (internal where possible). If this can only be achieved externally, then this should be done via the commissioners of the investigation and a relevant executive of the organisation.

6.1.3 Document security

Versions of the report to the investigation team

If the draft report is to be emailed to members of the investigation team then the draft should be password protected to open but left unlocked for team members to comment using "track changes". It is the author's practice to send almost completed drafts to clinical advisors she works with on a sequential basis, so that she can review and consider the comments of one advisor before taking receipt of the comments of another. This stepped approach is essential if the team are using track changes. Using the line reference function in Microsoft Word can aid the smoothness of the feedback process.

Versions of the report to interviewees and stakeholders

When the report is at a stage of development (i.e. final or penultimate draft) to be circulated to key interviewees and stakeholders, then it should be encrypted so that no one can tamper with its content.

People must not be able to open the document without a password.
There is no reason why the same password as has been used for the investigation team cannot be retained for this. However those who are more cautious may prefer to devise a new password.

The password should be recorded in a safe place by the report author, in a uniquely marked folder within the electronic storage system for all the investigation papers is probably the best place.

The password should consist of a combination of letters (lower and upper case), numbers and punctuation marks for maximum security.

In all cases

- The password to open the document must be sent via a separate email or medium and not with the report document.
- A secure email account should be used where possible if the report is being sent outside of the local organisation.

Example 1: RCA investigation report content template

Chapter heading or component of report	**Suggested content**
Acknowledgments and names and titles of the investigation team	
Index	Full list of chapter headings and main sub headings with correct page numbering
Acronyms	List of all acronyms used in the report
Executive summary	This should set out a summary of the incident, the purpose of the report, and main findings and conclusions of the investigation team
Chapter 1: Introduction	This should set out: 1. The purpose of the report and who it was commissioned by 2. A brief overview of the incident and its consequences 3. A summary of the patient/client/service user contact with the service
Chapter 2: Terms of reference for the investigation	The terms of reference should be set out in full
Chapter 3: Contact with involved others such as family members	This section should set out what efforts were made to contact family members, etc, and how they have been involved in the investigation. Any information contributed by the family can also be included here if appropriate
Chapter 4: The findings of the investigation	This section should set out: 1. The overall perspective of the Investigation Team 2. Any positive feedback to the health/social care professionals 3. The main care/case management concerns 4. The contributory factors identified for each case/care management concern 5. The identified root causes to each care/case management concern

	Note: If the investigation has aimed to answer core questions posed in the terms of reference, then these replace point 3. If one's findings are that things were not done as they should have been, you should still have contributory factors and root causes for the things not done well
Chapter 5: Any actions or improvements already implemented or in the process of being implemented	This chapter should set out any improvement work already in place, underway, or completed
Chapter Six: Conclusions	This chapter should set out the overall conclusions of the investigation team in relation to the terms of reference. The investigation team may or may not be able to make a statement about the predictability and preventability of the incident.
Chapter 7: Recommendations	Recommendations
Appendices	The appendices should include: 1. The full chronology of contacts between the patient/client/service user and the health/social care service. 2. The investigation methodology, including any specific investigation techniques used. 3. The information used to inform the investigation team's findings
Glossary and bibliography	All referenced texts should be detailed here. It is also useful to provide an overview of any specific technical data/terms here.

6.1.4 Other considerations

Make sure you have a well laid out facing page for your report that details:

- the title of the report
- the date of the final report
- the organisation name and logo (generally top right hand corner, or bottom right hand corner)

The NPSA has specific requirements it has set out in its recently reissued investigation report template for the "comprehensive" investigation, previously referred to as a level 2 investigation.

In addition to the core elements set out in the example report framework above, the NPSA requires (2010):

- a pre-investigation risk assessment;
- clarity about the level of investigation;
- support provided for the staff involved, and the extent of their involvement;
- post-investigation risk assessment;
- arrangements for sharing the learning;
- a distribution list for the report; and
- an action plan.

For an NHS trust, or a social care organisation these additional requirements must be met. However, it may be possible for these issues to be addressed more effectively in an addendum to the main investigation report.

With regard to the distribution of the report it is the experience of the author that investigation reports are often not widely circulated within local organisations. NHS and social care organisations may wish to consider publishing a copy of the executive summary of comprehensive reports for wider circulation.

Appendices

Appendix one:

Some easy to use Investigation and RCA Tools that support structured problem solving and structured data analysis

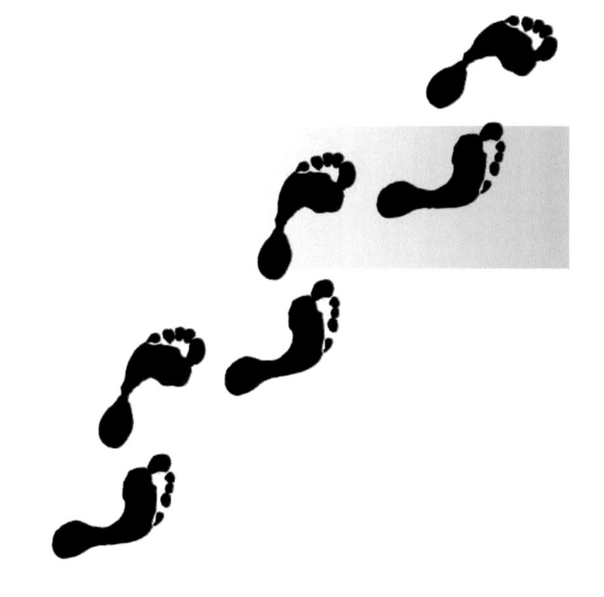

Introduction

The main body of this book has presented the essential phases of an effective investigation. It has also set out one of the most widely used investigation tools, the Timeline. However there are a range of additional tools and techniques that are also invaluable to the tool kit of the investigator. For ease of reference these tools and techniques are presented here.

The tools and techniques covered in this section are:

- Brain Storming (commonly becoming referred to as 'thought showers')
- Brain Writing
- Cause and Effect Charting
- Nominal Group Technique
- Five Why's
- Human Factors Analysis Framework
- Control Analysis

A1.1 Brainstorming and Brainwriting

Brainstorming will be a familiar technique that can be used to assist in the context of an 'around the table' post incident meeting to assist a group in identifying the issues that they believe require further exploration.

Brainstorming can also be used in this context to identify the influencing factors to a problem or event in conjunction with the following:

- The Five Whys' technique
- Human Factor Analysis
- Control Analysis

There are two main approaches to Brainstorming - Structured and Unstructured.

Structured Brainstorming

This is where the facilitator asks each individual in turn to contribute a suggestion or idea. Structured Brainstorming can enable less dominant members of a group participate. However 'putting' less confident persons on the spot can generate a 'nil response'.

Unstructured Brainstorming

This is essentially the 'free for all' commonly used in group meetings. Whilst it enables spontaneity and free thinking, it can result in ideas being lost and disorder amongst the group.
There are no right or wrong answers with brainstorming and the key to successful brainstorming is not to allow any in-depth questioning, or exploration of ideas during the 'brain storm'. The focus must be on the participants contributing their ideas. The time for clarification comes once all members have contributed and the process is exhausted.
It is essential that the facilitator record the ideas as they are spoken. Whilst the purest approach is to undertake the grouping of duplicates afterwards, in healthcare, the time constraints are such that the facilitator may well choose to undertake this as ideas are presented.
The advantages of brainstorming are that it generates:

- a list of 'problem' areas;
- a list of possible cause/ influencing factors;
- a list of potential consequences if 'problems' remain unaddressed;
- a list of potential solutions / remedies;
- encourages participation in the RCA process, and therefore feelings of ownership; and
- can be used to support the application of other techniques, e.g. Cause & Effect Charting and the Fishbone.

The disadvantages of brainstorming are it:

- can stagnate - therefore allow only one period of 'prolonged' silence;
- dominant persons can deter the contribution of other members;
- makes sensitive issues difficult to explore;
- does not protect anonymity; and
- increases the risk of non-validated information being used during the analysis of the critical problems identified during the incident review.

If there are problems in reaching a consensus with Brain Storming, the Nominal Group Technique can be used. (See A1.2)

Brain Writing

This technique can be applied as for Brainstorming; however, Brain Writing affords participants confidentiality and anonymity. It is also a way of overcoming the reticence of some members to contribute, if, for example, they feel inhibited by more senior persons in the room, or if there are personality tensions. Our experience is that it is a technique that works well in such situations and it is one that is easy for the facilitator to manage. It is the experience of the author that Brain Writing enables the maintenance of privacy and anonymity for individuals and this increases participant's willingness and ability to share their experience, thoughts and ideas.

Ways to use Brain Writing

During a facilitated team incident review/ 'round-the-table' discussion:

Once the chronological timeline has been digested, all participants are provided with blank post cards. They are asked to brainstorm their personal ideas on this card, e.g., additional questions about the sequence of events, or surrounding circumstances, problem areas, Care Management/Delivery Problems[11] etc. It is important that participants are given a specified time period in which to complete this and are asked not to discuss their thoughts with the persons sitting closest to them. All participants must be encouraged to have sufficient personal space for this exercise so that privacy is assured.

Once the allocated time period has passed, the group can take a recess while the facilitator

[11] C. Vincent, Dr S Adams et al. Clinical Risk Unit and Association of litigation and Risk Manager's Investigation Protocol. Royal Society of Medicine

collects the cards and writes everyone's ideas onto a flip chart, grouping them appropriately. This allows the collective thoughts of the group to be displayed.

If there are only a small number of issues, the facilitator may be able to lead the group through the techniques of the Five Why's, Control Analysis or Human Factors Analysis in further exploring these. If, however, the issues are numerous, as they frequently can be, the participants will need to prioritise the list so that the next stage in the process, i.e., the identification of influencing factors, can take place. The most effective technique for achieving a consensus as to the priorities, in these circumstances, seems to be the Nominal Group Technique. It is quick and easy to apply and enables the time available to the facilitator to be used to best effect.

Using Brain Writing in a Comprehensive Investigation

Conducting group interviews during a comprehensive investigation can be time efficient and enable the investigator access to a wide range of thoughts and perspectives. However the investigator needs to ensure that data robustness is not compromised. Brain Writing can assist with this. Where the investigator wants (or needs) to collect individual perspectives around specific areas of practice or service delivery he/she can pose a set of predesigned questions on a flip chart in the meeting room. Attendees can be asked to write their personal response to the questions on paper provided for this. The answer to each question should be set out on a separate sheet of paper. If an investigator wants to be able to triangulate the information provided he/she may want to consider providing each participant with a different colour paper. So if there are 10 people participating then there needs to be 10 different colours of paper. Whether or not participants say who they are is something the investigator needs to consider. Anonymity within an agreed set of rules is acceptable. If staff are required to say who they are then confidentiality of the data should be assured within agreed parameters, and participants must know how the information is to be used.

Note: The concept set out here could be used in advance of any individual face-to-face interviews. Furthermore the principles espoused could be used to request written information from a range of staff who may have useful perspectives but who do not need to, attend a face to face meeting.

A1.2 Nominal Group Technique (NGT)

Nominal Group technique is a consensus-building tool. It can be used at three distinct phases of the investigation process.
Firstly, it can be used to assist participants to prioritise the problems or issues that they consider to have been the most significant in contributing to the event occurring.
Secondly, it can be used to assist the group in agreeing the most fundamental causal factors contributing to each of the problems identified if consensus is hard to reach.
Finally, it can be used to agree the priority improvement recommendations &/or strategies arising from the causal analysis[23].
As a technique, it provides opportunity for all participants to vote, undeterred by stronger or more vociferous group members. In other words it avoids the 'he who shouts loudest' syndrome.

Rules

There is only one rule with this technique and that is that the participants agree to be bound by the results of the process. 'Sour grapes' are not acceptable.

Process

Step One

Utilising the Brain Writing technique detailed above, the participants are asked to identify the problems, or issues, present in the incident chronology, the priority problems, or the priority improvement opportunities.

Step two

The facilitator records all the suggestions onto a flip chart, white board or other aid. Once any duplicate issues have been eliminated and any sensible grouping of issues has taken place, the individual items on the final list are assigned a unique identifier, normally a letter or number.

Step three

Each participant is given a ranking card and is asked to select a pre-defined number of issues or problems, (generally not less than 5 and not more than 7), that they believe are the most significant. These are then ranked in order of priority with 1, being for the most important, and, 5 - 7 being for the least important. It is important that participants understand that they are required to record the unique identifier only, and not the description of the problem or idea they are ranking. This makes it much easier for the facilitator to collate the results. If participants record the 'description', mapping the results can be very time consuming, and this time usage cannot be afforded in this exercise.

Step four

The facilitator collects all of the cards at the end of the specified time period and collates the numbers of votes and the points for each of the problems or issues rated. Those receiving the highest numbers of votes, and the lowest score(s), will form the agreed list of prioritised issues that will be subject to causal analysis in the time left to the meeting.

[23] Affinity Mapping also works very well for prioritising the most important safety and quality improvement recommendations.

Equipment

The only equipment required for this activity is a flip chart or whiteboard, and sufficient plain paper upon which the participants can record their prioritised list.

It is a good idea to ask participants to divide their piece of paper in half, with one half entitled, Problem/Idea code and the other entitled Priority Rating.

Priority Rating

It is a good idea for the facilitator to map out a grid for recording the results of the exercise whilst participants are generating their priority lists. Such a grid might look like:

Code	Issue / Problem	Votes	Total votes	Points	Total
A	Failure to follow policy	......	10	1,2,2,1,2,3	17
B	No dedicated emergency bleeps	......	6	2,3,2,2,3,1	13
C	No trained staff	......	10	1,1,1,1.....	10
D	No environmental risk assessment	......	4	2,3,4,2,5,6	22

Reflection

If the above seems like 'hard work' you can always undertake this exercise on a straight number counting basis and ignore the relationship between the numbers of persons who have voted for the issue or problem, and the level of importance attached to this. You must however be mindful that this will reduce the robustness of the process.

Challenges the facilitator may experience using NGT

Whilst NGT is a highly adaptable voting and consensus building tool, it can bring challenge to the investigator/RCA facilitator. It is possible for there to remain considerable variation in the perceived priority of the identified problems or issues being considered for deeper exploration, in spite of the NGT technique being applied. Should this arise, the best the facilitator can do is to add up the total number of points awarded to each of the issues, sift out the obvious outliers and repeat the process, asking the participants to identify their top three issues out of the remaining issues, 1 being the most important. To minimise the amount of time this takes, it is advisable for the facilitator to ask one of the group members to assist with the mapping exercise. There is no risk of 'inter-group' 'breach of confidence' as the data will already be coded.

Prioritisation of recommendations and improvement strategies

A further area of challenge can arise when NGT is used to prioritise the range of improvement strategies considered necessary to remedy the weaknesses identified as part of the problem exploration process. It is not uncommon for participants to identify issues that are 'outside' of their immediate control, for example, those that require senior management support, or the release of scarce funds, as the most important improvement strategies. In order to identify a balanced list of recommendations, and agreed actions, that reflects the things that local teams and departments can action, as well as those issues that need to be communicated to other persons, groups, or organisations, we advise that the facilitator undertake the prioritisation of the improvement strategies in two phases.

Phase One:
This allows participants to identify what they believe to be the essential improvements, regardless of cost or their ability to effect the change. The recommendations and/or actions that are out of the teams control can then be 'parked'.

Phase Two:
This requires participants to reappraise the list of recommended improvements and focus on those that they, or their team and department or service, have some control over and, thus, are issues that they can do something about.

This two tiered process enables high level recommendations to be made whilst maximizing the opportunity for the identification and ownership of more locally focused recommendations. It also embraces the principle aim of Root Cause Analysis, which is to implement solutions that will act on a range of causes to break the causal chain.

A1.3 The Five Why Technique

The Five Why technique has been widely expounded as a useful problem solving tool. However, it is the experience of the author and her colleagues that the tool is often too simplistic and linear. It appears to work reasonably well for straight forward process orientated problem solving but less well in complex situations with many influencing factors and points of causality.

How to conduct a Five Why Analysis

- Identify the problem
- Write 'why' at least five times on a sheet of paper leaving space for the recording of 'the answer'
- Ask the group gathered, or the interviewee why the problem occurred, and notate the response under the first 'Why'.
- Ask the group or interviewee another 'Why' question to enable a deeper understanding of how the problem occurred and record the response in the next space.
- Continue to ask 'Why' until it seems that you have a depth of understanding of how the problem occurred and why. Once you are satisfied that you have identified the 'root' of the problem or the most important influencing factor then the process can be stopped.

Note: If you are analysing a more complex problem you may need break it down into more manageable components before trying to apply the Five Why technique. The diagram on the following page illustrates this.

Diagrammatic example of the Five Why's technique

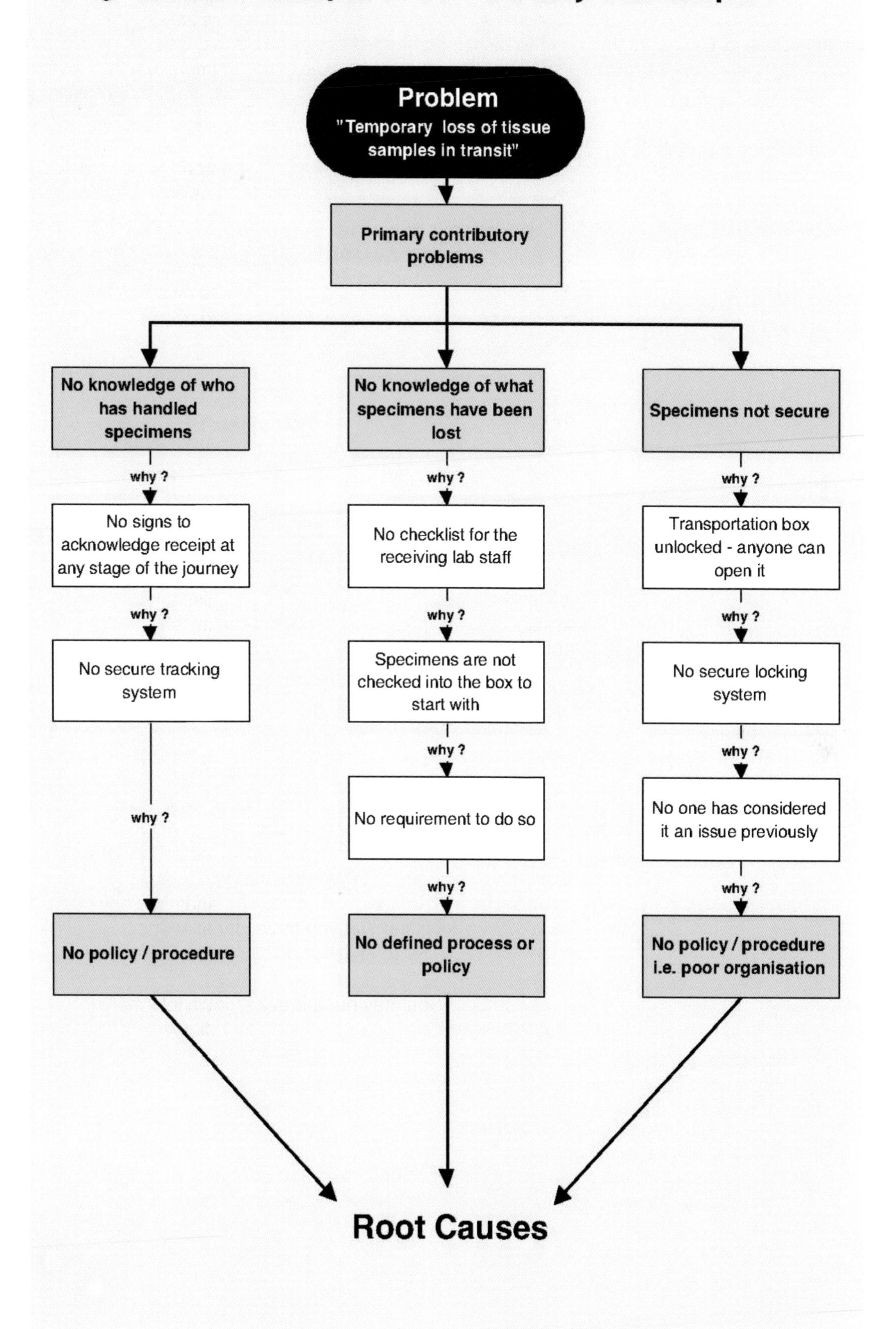

A1.4 The Cause and Effect Chart

There are many variations of cause and effect charts available in risk management and safety literature. The one presented in this text uses symbols to communicate the relationship between the data used to populate the chart and also to provide clarity about the nature of the data.

The cause and effect chart presented requires the following:

- clear knowledge of the sequencing of the antecedents to the incident;
- some evidence gathering to have been completed so that there is an understanding of the contributory factors to the incident; and
- a clearly defined range of symbols.

Cause and Effect charts are extensively used in industries, such as nuclear power, oil and aviation, to review and investigate accidents. They enable the visualisation of the incident as a whole including:

- The Timeline
- Influencing and causal factors
- Control failures

Essentially the Cause and Effect Chart allows one to chart the relationship of events, conditions, changes, controls and causal factors on a Timeline using standardised symbols for each. Consequently, the Cause and Effect chart is constructed to a specified format using defined features denoted by symbols and lines. These are depicted on the Cause Effect Chart on the following page.

How to Construct an Event and Causal Factor Chart

The steps detailed below were originally contributed by Dr Sally Adams from an unpublished document describing event and causal factor charting. What follows therefore are technical instructions on how to construct a Cause and Effect Chart.

Step 1: Define scope of chart from initial information available about the incident.

- Initiating event (I.e. the start of the incident's journey)
- Terminal event (The incident being investigated).

Step 2: Assess the initial information and documentation for completeness and content.
Consider the following:

- What happened?
- When did it happen?
- How did it happen?
- What were the consequences?

Step 3: Begin constructing the preliminary primary event line (as for a Timeline).Then insert secondary events (supporting information and other happenings not part of the direct sequence of events) and conditions (for example working conditions, availability of equipment, the skill mix of staff see page 67) into the chart at the appropriate places along the timeline.

Step 4: Gather new facts and add to chart

- As you proceed through the evaluation process you will discover new information that should be inserted into the chart at the correct location to show its relationship with the big picture. You may want to use some of the RCA tools to help you with this.
- Identify the underlying conditions and add these to the chart.

Step 5: Identify and add the causal factors and failed controls to chart

- Integration of results from other techniques can be added here, e.g., Change and Control Analysis.
- Decide what actions were inappropriate.
- Verify that the facts presented support your conclusions.

Step 6: Identify corrective actions taken and needed

a. Based upon failed controls and causal factors.

b. Corrective actions must be supported by facts and be feasible.

Developing your own symbols

As previously highlighted, it is acceptable to work within the principles of Cause and Effect charting and to develop your own simplified symbols. However we recommend that you try utilising the specified format above before embarking on your own design.

Reflection

The whole idea of using symbology for mapping key aspects of the investigation findings is very appealing. However for complex incidents spanning significant time periods, it can make the process too complex and the finished product too busy. This being said, one can take the principles of formal cause and effect charting and utilise these in a Multi Disciplinary Team (MDT) incident review meeting. At least one of our RCA trainers has had great success utilising different shapes with clearly assigned meanings in applying RCA principles to the review of incidents within Learning Disabilities.

You may also find that taking part of the concept so that 'critical points' in the Timeline are made more prominent is helpful. For contained incidents (in terms of time span), you could consider using Microsoft Visio to map your Cause and Effect Chart as most of the symbols are contained within this package as standard.

Finally we have worked with a number of health professionals, who have devised their own 'slimline' symbology. This again is perfectly acceptable providing you have a clearly identifiable legend on your map. If you are going to do this, we would suggest that as an organisation you agree core symbols so that consistency can be achieved.

As with all of the tools before deciding whether this one is for you - TRY IT.

Example of a Cause and Effect chart

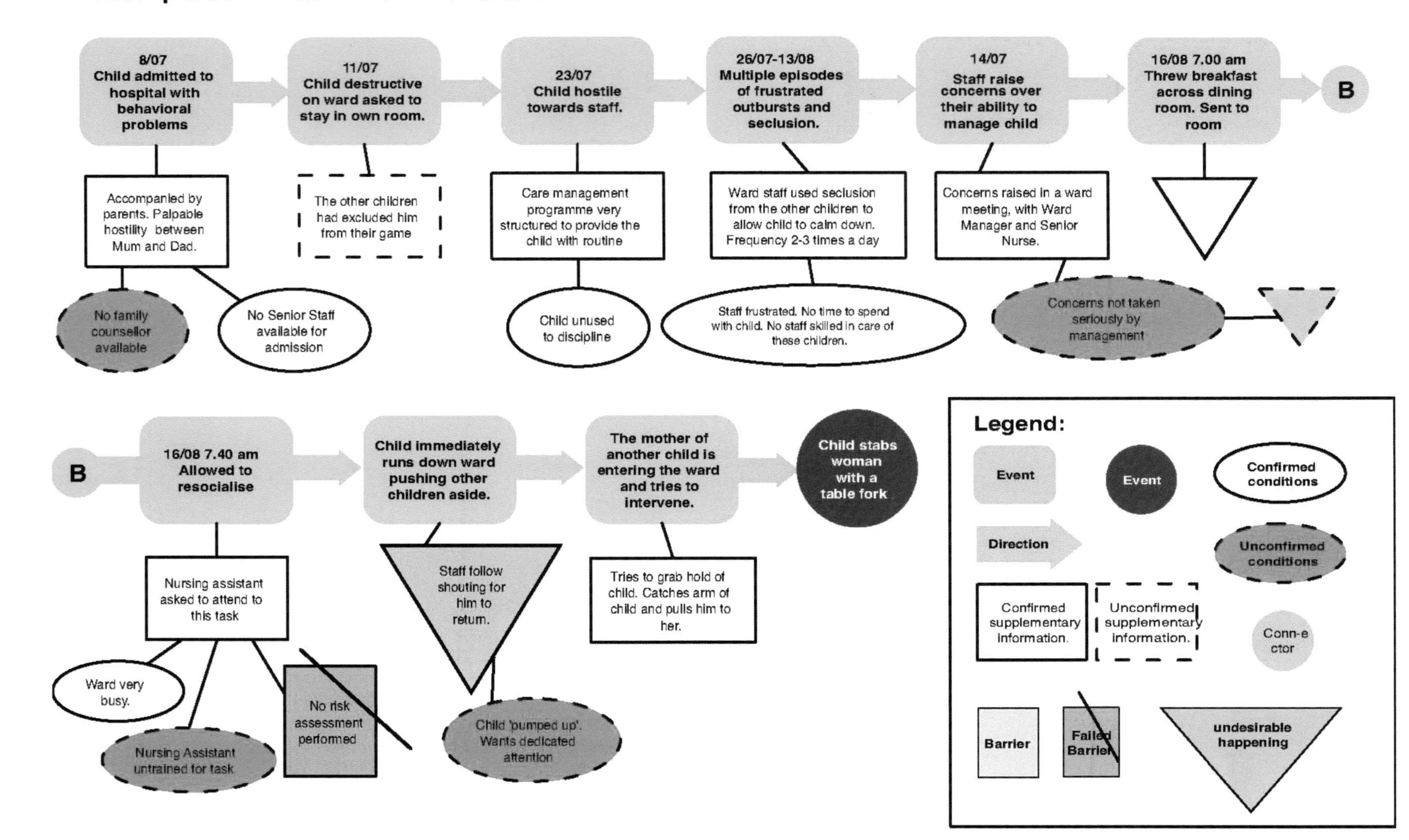

A1.5 The Fishbone Diagram

This a wonderful and versatile tool for the investigator. It can be used in a variety of ways:

- to assist in identifying a range of practice focused and systems based questions prior to interviewing staff;
- to enable a local team to look at aspects of their practice / case management that could have been improved and to understand how it could have been improved;
- to achieve clarity about the messages emerging from a range of interview data that has been assigned to a 'core question' or case management concern; and
- to analyse a range of interview and observational data to allow core themes to emerge.

Drawing the Fishbone

A common approach is to draw a long horizontal arrow onto a large white board or sheet of paper. At the head of the arrow is the problem to be explored, spines are then added to the arrow. Each spine is given a classification label representing the main areas under which you might want to explore the contributory factors to the identified problem.
The labels demonstrated on the fish below are based on those classifications originally advocated by the Clinical Risk Unit and Association of Litigation and Risk Managers and subsequently refined and adopted by the NPSA. However, others might be as simple as:

- Patient
- Personnel
- Environment
- Work Methods[12]

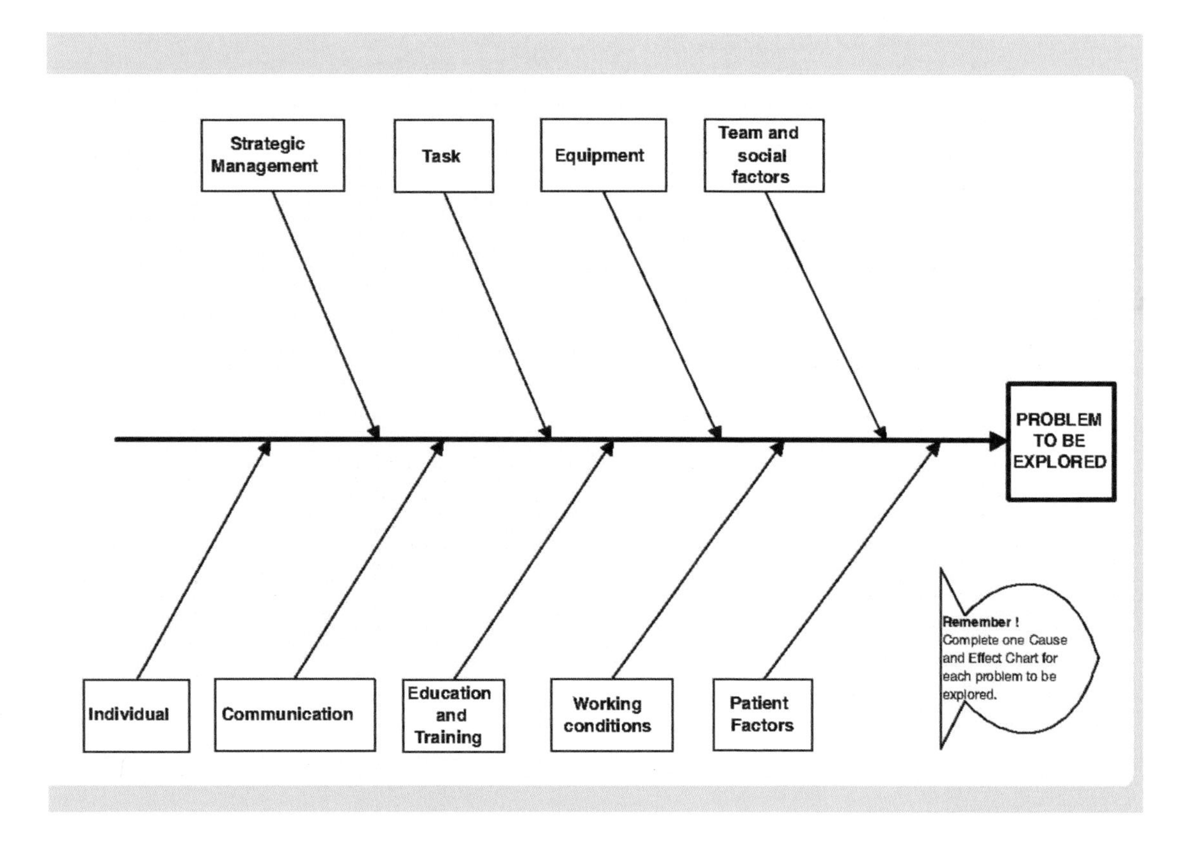

[12] Root Cause Analysis in Healthcare, Tools and Techniques. Joint Commission on Accreditation in Healthcare Organisations 2000.

The classification labels developed by Dr Ishikawa[13] in the mid 1960's are useful for analysing problems commonly associated with mechanical incidents, health and safety based, and estates based events.

These are:
The 4 M's: Methods, Machines, Materials, and Manpower
The 4 P's: Place, Procedure, People, and Policies
The 4 S's: Surroundings, Suppliers, Systems, and Skills.

You may be becoming aware that there is no universally accepted classification system and it would be inappropriate for such a classification system to be bound in tablets of stone. However, if you review the systems available, you will observe a common thread between them. For UK health providers, the accepted standard has been set by the NPSA. However, even if you adopt this model there will be occasions where it will need adaptation to meet the needs of the problem(s) you are exploring. This is especially so for investigations involving a range of agencies and involving a range of social and family factors. The NPSA framework does not naturally accommodate these issues.

It is possible to create classification headings for specific event types and the early work of James Reason[14] makes good argument as to the necessity of this. Quite simply he asserts that rarely is one classification framework going to meet all needs.

An example of a classification framework, devised specifically for an event analysis, can be found in the JACHO[15] book in relation to a child's abduction. The headings used were:

- Nursing issues
- Parental issues
- Employee security issues
- Visitor issues
- Abductor issues.

However, before 'branching out' and devising bespoke headings we recommend that your organisation agrees to work with an established causal analysis framework such as that promoted by the NPSA and that you work within this as far as is possible until you are confident in your understanding and application of this. In addition to the consistency such agreement brings, a systematic and common approach across an organisation makes the audit of this particular aspect of the incident investigation process much more achievable.

Challenges

A challenging feature of some classification frameworks is the lack of clarity regarding the placing of some commonly occurring influencing factors. The NPSA headings, listed below, are accompanied by tables that provide greater detail about the issues it believes falls under each heading.

- Patient (Child, Older Person, Family, Service User)
- Individual (staff member)
- Team and Social
- Equipment
- Work conditions
- Task / process
- Communication

---

[13] North Carolina Dept. of Environmental and Natural Resources. Fishbone diagram. A problem analysis tool. http://quality.enr.state.nc.us/tools/fishbone.htm

[14] Human Error James Reason Cambridge University Press 1990.

[15] Root Cause Analysis in Healthcare; Tools and Techniques. Joint Commission on Accreditation in Healthcare Organisations p.133 (2000)

- Education and Training
- Corporate Strategy

In our experience persons evolving their investigation skills find it easiest to work with the NPSA's model for this reason.

A1.5.1 Using the fishbone to analyse the contributory factors of clearly identified problems or to map out data that enables the investigator to logically set out an evidence based response to a 'key question' posed in the terms of reference to the investigation.

In a group meeting

The easiest way to identify the influencing factors for each problem identified is to consider each classification heading in turn and identify whether or not there were any issues of influence that map under it. Whilst brainstorming normally works well for this, if this is being undertaken with a group of participants and there are sensitivities in the room, the brain writing technique can easily be applied. Indeed there may be significant benefits to this if time availability is limited.

For example:
In the Absconsion incident detailed earlier in this book, one of the core problems identified may have been that the prescribed nursing observations were not conducted in a timely way, or that they were delayed.

This then would go in the 'problem' box at the head of the 'Fish'. E.g. "Timed Nursing Observations were delayed"

Then you would look at each spine of the fishbone and the label given to this e.g. Task Factors, and ask whether there were any task issues that contributed to the delay in conducting the Timed observations. If yes, note them, if No move onto the next 'spine'. This might for example be 'organisational factors'. If you have identified cultural or custom and practice issues that did contribute to the problem you may choose to notate them on this spine.

Normally you would continue in this way until you feel that as a group you have thoroughly reflected on the specific 'problem' you are analysing. Then, you would move to the next identified problem, and do a separate fishbone for that. Continuing, until all problems identified have been analysed.

Note 1: Staff will often identify factors that ameliorated the problem these factors should be noted and differentiated from those factors that were contributory to the problem, e.g. by writing them in a different colour, or by putting a 'tick' by them. It is important that these factors are not lost. The presentation of these factors will bring balance to the investigation report you will subsequently write.

Note 2: A contributory factors framework is presented in the following section. Making this available to staff [present at a post incident reflective meeting can facilitate the identification of contributory factors and those of amelioration to the problems being analysed.

Note 3: Some people do not like working with the fishbone diagram but prefer a table or other format for documenting the outputs of the process. There is no impediment to this. It is the principle of the process that is important and that the choice of documentation style makes the analysis easy to read.

A1.6 Contributory Factors and a Human Factors Framework[31]

As should now be clear to you, a fundamental part of the RCA investigation is the identification of the contributory and causal factors that contributed to the incident's occurrence, and/or specific problems identified within the sequencing of events.

The significance of a contributory factor (or group of factors) will vary from being highly significant to the chain of events, or 'care or case management problem' identified, to mildly significant. It is only when you have mapped out the full range of contributory factors that you can begin to consider what factors were of most significance or indeed at the root of the problem.

As set out in A1.5 'contributory factor' information is aligned to one of the primary classification headings detailed in the tables that follow. The contributory factor information may be shared verbally during a reflective 'round the table' discussion as suggested in section A1.5, or via the analysis of interview transcripts. (see Step Four of the investigation process).

The following NPSA tables, based on the CRU/ALARM[16] protocol, detail the sorts of issues you may wish to consider when examining particular concerns or problems for underlying influencing or causal factors.

Individual Factors:

These are factors that the individual(s), involved in an event, bring that are unique to them. They are often termed as personality factors but in reality individual factors are much more than this. They include psychological factors, home factors, work relationship factors and many more.

Individual Factors	Components
Physical issues	General Health (e.g. nutrition, diet, exercise, fitness) Physical disability (e.g. eyesight problems, dyslexia) Fatigue
Psychological Issues	Stress (e.g. distraction / preoccupation) Specific mental health illness (e.g. Depression) Mental impairment (e.g. illness, drugs, alcohol, pain) Motivation (e.g. boredom, complacency, low job satisfaction) Cognitive factors (e.g. attention deficit, distraction, preoccupation, overload)
Social Domestic	Domestic / lifestyle problems
Personality Issues	Low self confidence / over confidence Gregarious / interactive, reclusive Risk averse / risk taker

[16] C. Vincent, Dr S Adams et al Clinical Risk Unit and Association of Litigation and Risk Managers Investigation Protocol. Royal Society of Medicine pages 20-23 (1999)

Team and Social Factors

Team factors predominantly involve communication issues. However management style, traditional hierarchical structures and lack of respect for less senior team members and less qualified workers can significantly affect the cohesiveness of the team. Perception of role both own and others also affects team functionality.

Team Factors	Components
Role Congruence	Is there parity of understanding Are role definitions correctly understood Are roles clearly defined
Leadership	Is there effective leadership - clinically Is there effective leadership - managerially Can the leader lead Are leadership responsibilities clear and understood Is the leader respected
Support and cultural factors	Are there support networks for staff Team reaction to adverse events Team reaction to conflict Team reaction to newcomers Team openness
Perception	What is the perception of team? (uni-professional, multi-professional, how is 'team' understood)

Communication Factors

Did any aspect of verbal, non-verbal or written communications contribute to poor performance, the occurrence of the event, or the containment of this issue?

Communication Factors	Components
Verbal communication	Verbal commands / directions unambiguous Tone of voice and style of delivery appropriate to situation Correct use of language Made to appropriate person(s) Recognised communication channels used (e.g. head of service).
Written communication	Are records easy to read Are all relevant records stored together and accessible when required Are the records complete and contemporaneous Are memo's circulated to all members of team Are communications directed to the right people
Non verbal communication	Body Language issues (closed, open, aggressive, relaxed, stern faced)

Task Factors

Task factors are those that support and aid in the safe and effective delivery of particular functions within the healthcare process(es).

Task Factors	Components
Guidelines Procedures and Policies	Up-to-date Available at appropriate location (e.g. accessible when needed) Understandable / useable Relevant; Clear; Unambiguous; Correct Content; Too Complex; Outdated; Unavailable/missing; Unrealistic Adhered to / followed Appropriately targeted (i.e. aimed at right audience)
Decision making aids	Availability of such aids e.g. CTG machine, risk assessment tool, fax machine to enable remote assessment of results Access to senior / specialist advice Easy access flow charts and diagrams Complete information - test results, informant history
Procedural or Task Design	Do the guidelines enable one to carry out the task in a timely manner Do staff agree with the 'task/procedure design' Are the stages of the task such that each step can realistically be carried out

Education and Training

The availability of and quality of the training programmes available to all staff can directly affect their ability to perform to their job specification and respond appropriately under difficult or emergency circumstances. The effectiveness of 'training' as a method of safety improvement is also affected by content, delivery style, and assessment of skill acquisition, monitoring and updates.

Education and Training	Components
Competence	Adequacy of knowledge Adequacy of skills Length of experience Quality of experience Task familiarity Testing and Assessment
Supervision	Adequacy of supervision Adequacy of mentorship
Availability / accessibility	On the job training Emergency Training Team training Core skills Training Refresher courses
Appropriateness	Content Target audience Style of delivery Time of day provided

Equipment Factors

In the healthcare context, it is essential that we can rely upon the functionality of equipment provided to deliver care to patients. Resource both in terms of appropriately skilled personnel, monies to enable the implementation of training regimes, the purchase of new equipment, etc, also directly impact upon performance and the propensity for error.

Equipment	Components
Displays	Correct information Consistent and clear information Legible information Appropriate feedback No interference
Integrity	Good working order Appropriate size Trustworthy Effective safety features Good maintenance programme
Positioning	Correctly placed for use Correctly stored
Usability	Clear controls User manual Familiar equipment New equipment Standardisation

Working Conditions

Working conditions are all of those factors affecting your ability to function at optimum levels in the work place

Work Environment Factor	Components
Administrative factors	The general efficiency of administrative systems e.g. reliability Systems for requesting medical records Systems for ordering drugs Reliability of administrative support
Design of physical environment	Office design: computer chairs, height of tables, anti-glare screens, security screens, panic buttons, placing of filing cabinets, storage facilities, etc. Area design: length, shape, visibility, cramped, spacious
Environment	Housekeeping issues - cleanliness Temperature Lighting Noise levels
Staffing	Skill mix Staff to patient ratio Workload / dependency assessment Leadership Use Temporary staff Retention of staff / staff turnover

Work Environment Factor	Components
Work load and hours of work	Shift related fatigue Breaks during work hours Staff to patient ratio Extraneous tasks Social relaxation, rest and recuperation
Time	Delays caused by system failure or design Time pressure

Organisational Factors

These are factors that are either inherent or embedded within the organisation. Often these factors are latent, normally non-problematic and only come to light when adversity strikes.

Organisational Factors	Components
Organisational structure	Hierarchical structure, not conducive to discussion, problem sharing, etc. Tight boundaries for accountability and responsibility Clinical versus the managerial model
Culture Priorities	Dynamic, forward thinking, developmental, experimental Safety driven External assessment driven e.g. Star Ratings Financial balance focused
Externally imported risks	Locum / Agency policy and usage Contractors Equipment loan PFI
Safety culture	Safety / efficiency balance Rule compliance Terms and Conditions of Contracts Leadership example (? Visible evidence of commitment to safety) Open culture

Patient Factors

Patient factors tend to be those issues that are unique to the patient, or patients, involved in the event. They, like individual factors, are often grouped into social and cultural factors. Existing co-morbidity is also a significant factor in these taxonomic components.

Patient Factors	Components
Clinical condition	Pre-existing co-morbidity Complexity of condition Seriousness of condition Treatability
Social factors	Culture / religious beliefs Life style (smoking/ drinking/ drugs/diet) Language Living accommodation (e.g. dilapidated) Support networks
Patient Factors	**Components**
Physical factors Mental/ psychological factors	Physical state - malnourished, poor sleep pattern, etc. Motivation (agenda, incentive) Stress (family pressures, financial pressures) Existing mental health disorder Trauma
Interpersonal relationships	Staff to patient and patient to staff Patient to patient Inter family - siblings, parents, children

Verification of Causal Factors

Whilst undertaking a causal analysis is a relatively straightforward process, there are some pitfalls of which one should be aware.

It is very tempting, when undertaking a causal analysis, to bring in data that is not related to the precise problem you are analysing. It is essential that all contributory factors are authenticated as belonging to the problem to which it/they have been aligned. In a reflective group scenario brain writing assists with this as one can more easily validate the factor by seeing how many people have made a similar observation. If you are working with interview records then you should find that there is similar information extracted as 'contributory' from more than one interview.

If you do not check of the validity of the information via a triangulation process there is a risk that the robustness of your findings may be compromised and the credibility of the investigation questioned. Furthermore, missing out the validation/triangulation process may result in the wrongful identification of 'root causes' which would mean that any recommendations made may also be misdirected.

A1.7 Control Analysis

Step Two of the Investigation Process highlights the central place of Timelining in the analysis of incidents where there is a sequence of events that needs to be understood. However, Step Two also highlights the limitations of Timelining and incident types that are better suited to Control analysis.

What Control Analysis is, and how to do it is presented here.

Control Analysis is a problem solving technique that enables an investigator or quality assurance professional to look at all of the control measures / control defences in a system or process e.g. managing a request for access to confidential information and to determine the robustness of each control measure, and also the vulnerability of the process if any one, or group of control measures should fail.

Control Analysis can be used before an incident has ever occurred as a quality / safety management tool. It does not need to be confined to the toolkit of the investigator.

What is a Control Measure

Control measures are designed to prevent harm to people, buildings, organisations and communities. Other common terminologies for 'Controls' in this sense are 'defences' or 'barriers'. Controls can be physical, natural, human action or administrative in nature[17].

Physical controls are the most reliable in terms of providing a failsafe solution to safety problems, followed by controls using distance time and place. Human Action Controls and Administrative Controls tend to be weak in terms of failsafe. This is because they rely upon human performance for their success and we are not all that reliable in the consistency of our performance. This is not to say that we should not consider, and use, human action and administrative controls rather we should be more aware of their inherent dangers and ensure that we put in place other mechanisms to support the effectiveness of these control measures.

For example, if one way of preventing future failure is to implement a training programme, this in itself is weak in terms of failsafe. However, one can make the measure more effective by ensuring:

- It is targeted at the right people.
- That mandatory means mandatory.
- That the programme incorporates an assessment of understanding and competency following the programme.
- That the programme content is correctly defined and targeted to identified need.
- That the person(s) delivering the programme are competent to do so.
- The need for refresher training and the timing of this is clearly defined.
- There is a clearly defined process for evaluating the effectiveness and impact of the training programme. An example of good practice in this area is in the ambulance service, where paramedics must demonstrate not only competence but also the degree of use of the acquired skills. If skill usage is below that required to assure competence then refresher training and assessment is required for skill maintenance.

[17] Physical Controls = Hot water pipe lagging, Administrative Controls = Policies and Procedures, Training programmes etc, Human Action = undertaking nursing observations, checking the temperature of bath water, Natural Controls = Controls associated with time and place. E.g. Community Pharmacists allow a period of time to elapse before rechecking a drug prior to dispensing.

A1.7.1 Application of Control Analysis

On page 73 is an example of the appropriate use of this analysis tool following the retention of swabs perineal suturing after childbirth.

In contained system failures such as this the investigator(s) may opt to solely perform a control analysis to optimise time and resource efficiency as well as delivering a credible analysis of 'what went wrong'.

How to conduct a post incident control analysis

Step 1

Define the end product. For example:

- The safe disposal of sharps.
- The administration of the right drug in the right dose, via the right route.
- Operating on the right patient and on the right body part
- The safe storage of confidential information on a Personal Computer (PC)

Step 2

Identify the core stages of the process. For example if you are looking at a drug safety issue, the core stages are production, purchase, storage, prescribing, dispensing and administration. Brainstorm all of the control measures that are in place to ensure that each stage is performed correctly.

For example if you are focusing on drug administration you would list at least the following:

- Policy and procedure
- Training programme
- Asking the patient
- Prescription chart
- Patient identifiers
- Equipment
- Competency assessment
- Checking procedure (1 nurse, 2 nurses etc)
- Clear legible writing

Step 3

Separate out the list into macro and micro[18] control measures, ensuring the linkage between each is clear. For example in the list above the policy and procedure and the training programme are macro control measures. Whilst asking the patient, competency assessment clear legible writing are micro control measures (i.e. subcomponents).

The templates on the following pages are designed to facilitate the mapping of this stage in the Control Analysis process. (N.B when using the template on page 75 use one template per macro control measure).

Step 4

Once you have mapped all of the macro and associated micro controls, you then need to consider, or, assess, the functionality of each micro control measure.

If you are doing this post incident, this may be relatively easy as there may be one of more controls that have failed allowing the incident to occur. If you are doing this 'pre-incident' you may need to explore how staff perceive the effectiveness of the controls in place and whether they actually adhere to them.

---

[18] A Macro measure is a 'large-scale' measure usually consisting of a variety of sub-components. A Micro measure is a 'small-scale' measure and is a specific sub-component of the Macro control.

For the analysis conducted pre-incident:
We suggest the application of a rating scale when assessing the functionality of each micro control measure. The following is an example of such a rating scale:

1. The control measure consistently performed as intended - i.e., it worked, the staff carried out this aspect of the process, etc
2. The control measure was invariably performed consistently but there was the occasional lapse.
3. Application and performance of the control measure are variable, a bit hit or miss.
4. The control measure is usually/was circumvented, i.e., missed out
5. There is no control measure.

Step 5

For those micro controls rated at 3, 4 or 5, the investigator, or investigation team, (+/- a wider group of stakeholders), should explore the reasons for this more fully so that the contributory factors to the underperformance can be identified and recommendations made to address these.

You may find that using the following will assist at this stage:

- Brain storming / brain writing
- Five why technique
- Application of a human factor framework.

The Advantages of Control Analysis

The advantage of the Control Analysis technique is that it keeps everyone's mind focused on the task in hand. It is also reasonably concise. Furthermore once a system or process has been mapped in detail it can be stored and retrieved should an adverse incident occur involving it.

The example Control analysis on the following page was performed after the investigation team had their RCA derailed because those present preferred to debate the management of Post Partum Haemorrhage.

Reflecting on the content of this analysis, it was agreed that the most important issues (root causes) were:

- The guideline directing this element of practice.
- The perceptions of health professionals regarding their role and responsibility and the lack of consistency in this between Gynaecology and Maternity, and the Labour Ward environment and Theatres.
- The robustness of the physical control.
- The weakness of the training process and competency assessment.

In terms of maximising the success of any safety improvement strategy, all of these issues would need to be targeted in the recommendations and agreed remedial actions required.

Factors for Success with Control Analysis

- To maximise the successful application of Control Analysis it is essential that all of the relevant stakeholders are invited to participate in the process. By this we mean all those persons, who perform the task, being analysed. It is the best way to avoid undertaking a superficial analysis and to maximise opportunity for identifying the macro and micro controls.
- If you are undertaking a Control Analysis on a large complex process such as Drug Safety, Data Protection, and the such like, we recommend that you try and break the process down into its constituent parts, and then undertake the Control Analysis on each of these. For example if one were undertaking an analysis on Drug Safety in an NHS health providing unit one might agree the following components to be analysed separately:
  - Purchasing of drugs
  - Drug storage
  - The dispensing process
  - The prescribing process
  - The administration process

If you do not do this it is possible that the task you have to undertake will become overly complex and cumbersome. Furthermore it is unlikely that you will succeed in 'pulling together' the right group of stakeholders if you do not break down the task into 'manageable chunks'.

A1.7.2 Pro-active Control Analysis

As mentioned previously, Control Analysis can be applied retrospectively or proactively. The process is exactly the same as described on the previous pages. The slight change comes at Step Four. Here the participants, to the process, would take a view on the usual situation. In my experience, if you have the right stakeholders taking part, they are usually quite honest regarding those micro controls that are not performing as well as they should, and there is often a clear understanding as to why this is.

Event: *Retained swab post perineal suturing* **Affected person Or thing:** *Patient Y*

POST INCIDENT CONTROL ANALYSIS

What prevention controls were in place ? (i.e. what control measures were there?)	Did the control work or fail?	If it failed then why?	How did the control failure affect the consequence of the event?
Swab Count	Failed	3 changes of staff. Dr's perceive this as a midwifery task. In main theatres it is a nurses task.	Direct adverse contribution
Pre, during, post-op count	Failed	Complacency of practice. Swabs too large to leave behind. Staff not required to document their checks.	Direct adverse contribution
Competency Assessment	Not undertaken for this activity	Competency assumed. Swab counts for this procedure not given same level of importance as for other operative procedures.	Direct adverse contribution
2 person checks	Failed	Often only one member of staff present.	Direct adverse contribution
Regular number of swabs per pack			
Size of swab	Failed	The size had been increased after the last similar event. But an abdominal tagged swab was thought to be too big.	Direct adverse contribution
Guidelines	Failed	Ambiguous, do not specify exact procedure, documentation of 'all present and correct' not required. Out of step with main theatres.	Direct adverse contribution

Example Template for a Post Incident Control Analysis [1]

The Incident?: **Impact of Incident:**

POST INCIDENT CONTROL ANALYSIS V1

What prevention controls were in place?	Did the Control work as intended or underperform / fail?	If it underperformed or failed what contributed to the underperformance / failure?	How significant an impact did the underperformance / failure of the control on the incident that subsequently occurred? And was it a 'root cause' or simply a 'contributory factor'

Example Template for a Post Incident Control Analysis where there are a range of substantial 'Macro' Controls to be analysed in detail [2]

The Incident?: ?: **Impact of Incident:**

Name of Control Process:

Macro Control number/name:

Micro(sub) controls Note 2	Did the micro control work as intended or underperform / fail ? Note 3	If it underperformed or failed what contributed to the underperformance / failure? Note 4	How significant an impact did the underperformance / failure of the control on the incident that subsequently occurred? And was it a 'root cause' or simply a 'contributory factor'

Recommendations:

Note 1 - Macro controls are your 'big' control measures e.g. A Policy; Training programmes; defined checking process etc Note 2 - e.g. specific checking mechanisms Note 3 - Functionality of stated controls in respect of this incident? i.e. 1=fully functional 2= reasonable performance 3= variable performance 4= unsatisfactory performance 5= control not present Note 4 - Consider using the 5 why technique, human factors framework etc

Example of a pre-incident (pro-active) Control Analysis targeting predicable hazards in the process
Process: The Safe Administration of Drugs

PRO-ACTIVE CONTROL ANALYSIS

Hazard or Hazards	What Controls or Defences are in place?	Additional Controls /Defences required?	What are the perceived priorities for safe practice?	Failsafe attributes ?Strong/Medium/ Weak	Improve by:	Cost Implications? Very High/ High/Medium/ Low/Very Low	Who's responsibility? Local dept Local manager Trust Committee Trust board
Wrong Drug	Two person checks	Bar coding	Drug policy	Weak	Review communication	L ✔	Clinical. Gov. Comm.
Wrong Patient	Ward based pharmacy checks	Electronic prescribing	Training	Weak/Medium	Assessments	M ✔	Training & Dev. Dept.
Wrong Dose	Patient ID bracelets	Use a 'time gap' between two person check	Check patient ID correct	Weak	Bar Coding	H - to RMC	Risk Man. Comm.(RMC)
Wrong route	Training		Two person checks	Weak	'time gap' between	L ✔	Clinical Gov. Comm.
Illegible drug chart	Patients own drugs and self administrati on		Electronic prescribing	Medium	Training and Audit	L ✔	Clinical Gov. Comm.
Explanatory notes:	**Activity:** The thing to be risk assessed **Target:** A thing or person of value that has been or could be hurt or damaged by the interaction of a harmful energy flow, or a harmful environment. **Hazard:** A danger or risk **Controls/Barriers/Defences:** Measures designed to prevent harm or damage. **Perceived importance (of control measure)**: Which of these additional desired control measures do you think are the most important to make the environment safer? **Failsafe attributes:** How effective do you think your control measures will be in preventing an accident or an incident occurring? Will they assist you in getting it 'right first time? **Decision:** Accept current situation / Reduce the risk / Eliminate the risk **Cost Implications:** What are the anticipated costs of implementing the chosen 'control measure'? This may vary according to each individual organisation, see table (right).					Costs: Very High/ High/ Medium/ Low/ Very Low:	

Template for a pre-incident (pro-active) Control Analysis targeting predicable hazards in the process

Process:

PRO-ACTIVE CONTROL ANALYSIS

Hazard or Hazards	What Controls or Defences are in place?	Additional Controls /Defences required?	What are the perceived priorities for safe practice?	Failsafe attributes ?Strong/Medium/ Weak	Improve by:	Cost Implications? Very High/ High/Medium/ Low/Very Low	Who's responsibility? Local dept Local manager Trust Committee Trust board
Explanatory notes:	**Activity:** The thing to be risk assessed **Target:** A thing or person of value that has been or could be hurt or damaged by the interaction of a harmful energy flow, or a harmful environment. **Hazard:** A danger or risk **Controls/Barriers/Defences:** Measures designed to prevent harm or damage. **Perceived importance (of control measure**): Which of these additional desired control measures do you think are the most important to make the environment safer? **Failsafe attributes:** How effective do you think your control measures will be in preventing an accident or an incident occurring? Will they assist you in getting it 'right first time? **Decision:** Accept current situation / Reduce the risk / Eliminate the risk **Cost Implications:** What are the anticipated costs of implementing the chosen 'control measure'? This may vary according to each individual organisation, see table (right).					Costs: Very High/ High/ Medium/ Low/ Very Low:	

Appendix 2:

General practice

Introduction

Whilst all of the principles of the investigation techniques apply equally to all types of healthcare providers, there are some special considerations for general practitioners (GPs) given the nature of their work. The common experience of GPs is the infrequent occurrence of category red events, however, general practices can experience frequently occurring events of lower severity, which do upset the efficient running of their services and the perception of the local community to whom they provide a service. Furthermore, these oft-occurring low risk events can be insidious, in the aggregate negative impact they have either on the healthcare professionals or on the well being of the patients affected.

Many GPs have subscribed to the Significant Event Audit (SEA) process advocated by Dr Jonathan Stead[19] and Dr Mark Pringle[20] upon which to build their adverse event systems. This appears to be well received and for many GPs is working well. The challenge of the SEA process, in terms of identifying the underlying causal factors, is the time available for it in the health centre setting. Not infrequently, this results in a moderate number of cases being reviewed within a single meeting, which may result in superficial analysis only, and not enable the participants to identify the improvement strategies that are going to provide best return for their efforts.

The following pages present a process that builds on the SEA process, but also allows the reporting member of staff to highlight what they believe to have been the key system, quality or human failures that directly contributed to its occurrence. In keeping with the ethos of SEA, incident reporters are also encouraged to report good practice events.

Enabling reporters to identify the issues they believe need to be addressed in order to effect a safer and improved quality service should provide scope for GPs, and their staff, to use their SEA time to best effect. The person identified within each constituent part of the GP practice or health centre, e.g. health centre, community pharmacy, etc, would collect the event notification forms as usual. Priority will naturally be given to those rating as being of high, or very high, risk.

Prior to the SEA meeting, this individual would circulate a list of the identified learning points and issues of concern to all practice members and ask that they be ranked in order of perceived priority. Some structure could be given to this, e.g., staff could be asked to rank the issues in terms of:

- level of risk to patient or staff safety;
- ongoing risk to smooth running of practice;
- increased levels of irritation, or stress associated with the problem; and
- the numbers of complaints received by clients/patients, etc.

[19] Grace Sweeney, Richard Westcott & Jonathan Stead, The Practice and Experience of Significant Event Audit in Primary Care" (2003) 'http://projects.exeter.ac.uk/sigevent/articles/pracandexp.html'

[20] Dr M Pringle et al (1995), "Significant Event Auditing: A study of the feasibility and potential of care-based auditing in primary medical care". The Royal College of General Practitioners *Occasional paper no. 70.*

Once the ranked lists have been returned, the identified lead can work out what the overall perceived priorities or major problems are. The SEA meeting can, therefore, be focused on these with a brief synopsis of the events leading to the identification of them presented to the group at the start, so that the context of how these issues were identified is maintained.
The root cause analysis tools best suited to the analysis process during the SEA process are:

- control analysis (see p.94)
- change analysis (see p.40)
- five why's technique (see p.80)

However, there will occasionally be some issues, or aggregated issues, that are more complex and it may be necessary to map out a full timeline and undertake a full causal analysis using the NPSA's *Contributory factors framework* headings. (Pages 32, 49-57, 88)

SIGNIFICANT EVENT RECORD FORM

This form should be used to record an event that you feel was significant. It can involve anything that affects the running of the practice – from administration to clinical care. It might be something that worked particularly well that could be adopted by others, it might be something that nearly went wrong, or something that did not go very well, and could have been dealt with better.
The most important thing to understand and remember is that if something has gone wrong, the aim is to support, to learn, and to improve - NOT TO BLAME. This is all about improving ourselves, our practice, and the care we offer our patients.

1 Name :
2 Date :
3 Date of event:
4 Patient Identifier: (if relevant)
5 Is this a 'good practice' event? Yes / No (If Yes go to Q7.)
6 Was there any harm (physical or psychological) or damage caused as a result of this event? (Mark/ select appropriate coloured box)

Very Low Risk | Low Risk | Moderate Risk | High Risk

7 Brief description of event, its antecedents and consequences: (continue on additional sheet if necessary)
8 Good practice points/learning points/key issues of concern:
9 Future risk associated with issue(s) if left unaddressed: (Mark/ select appropriate coloured box & see overleaf for guidance)

Very Low Risk | Low Risk | Moderate Risk | High Risk

Once completed, please hand this back to your practice lead for event analysis. It can then be considered for discussion at the practice clinical meeting.

Guidance Notes – for form completion

Glossary of the terms:

- No harm – speaks for itself;
- Minor harm/damage: this refers to temporary harm or damage remediable (or recovered from), within approximately 1 month;
- Moderate harm/damage: This may include semi-permanent damage, which will take a time period of +/- a year to recover from - recovery is expected;
- Major Harm: lifelong effect on lifestyle, quality of life, physical and mental well being, ability to provide service etc;
- Tragic harm/catastrophic damage: Potentially avoidable death, loss of health centre premises, Healthcare records stolen from GP's car.

Question 9 only refers to issues arising out of the Green, Yellow and Orange events – Red events should always result in some degree of formal review and formal report.

Here you need to think about the originating event, and the issues of concern/ learning points that you have identified. If the status quo is maintained what is the future risk of harm to you, your colleagues, your patients, the practice in terms of reputation, maintenance of client list and local confidence etc. It is a qualitative process and considered gut feeling based on experience is good enough.
The prompts below will assist you in answering Q9.
A - What is likelihood of recurrence? Choose one.

Level	Descriptor	Description
A	Certain	Likely to re-occur on many occasions. (Each organisation must decide on frequency values e.g. monthly, 12 times a year etc)
B	Likely	Will probably re-occur but not everyday event. (Each organisation to determine frequency values)
C	Possible	May re-occur occasionally. (Each organisation to determine frequency values)
D	Unlikely	Do not expect it to happen again but possible event. (Each organisation to determine frequency values)
E	Rare	Can't believe that this will ever happen again. (Each organisation to determine frequency values)

B – What is likely to happen if events happen again or status quo remains? Choose one box in all 3 columns - highest score wins

Descriptor	A Potential impact on individual(s)/ family members	B Potential impact on organisation + resource implications *** (each practice must consider level of severity)	C Number of persons affected at one time
1 Catastrophic / tragic	Death, suicide/ homicide	CQC visit; criminal prosecution; extended service closure; significant financial cost; national publicity	Many >50 e.g. vaccination error; screening errors /failure to recall
2 Major	Permanent injury/harm	Temporary service closure; long term staff sickness > 4 wks; Health & Safety Executive investigation; serious complaint anticipated; loss of family(s) from list.	Moderate numbers 16 – 50 e.g. lost specimens, hostage situation
3 Moderate	Semi-permanent injury/damage	Local adverse publicity; MDA reportable; Mental Health Act Commission assessment; staff sickness > 3 days; complaint anticipated.	Small numbers 3-15
4 Minor	Short Term Injury Or Damage	Minimal risk to organisation; Staff sickness < 3 days; low risk complaint.	1 – 2
5 Insignificant	No injury/adverse outcome	No risk at all to organisation.	N/A

Take your answer for A and your answer for B and plot on the graph below

	CONSEQUENCE				
LIKELIHOOD	**5 Insignificant**	**4 Minor**	**3 Moderate**	**2 Major**	**1 Tragic**
A – Almost certain					
B - Likely					
C - Possible					
D - Unlikely					
E - Rare					

Appendix 3:

More tips for successful investigative interviewing[21]

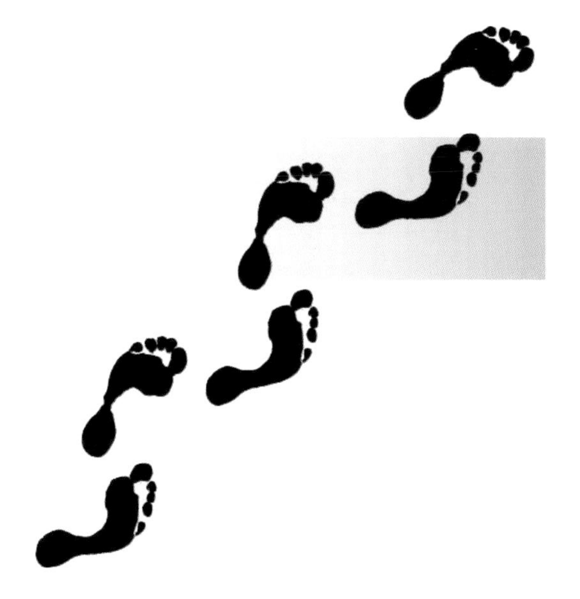

Introduction
When interviewing staff following an adverse event, we often adopt the interviewing style with which we are most comfortable. Not infrequently, this results in a series of short answer questions being asked of the interviewee, insufficient time for them to be able to respond and the interviewer maintaining control of the process. One of the reasons for this is that much of our interviewing experience is gained in interviewing people for jobs and the style is completely unsuitable for interviewing staff following an adverse event.

The following pointers are to assist you in reflecting upon your practice and to enable you to obtain as much information as possible from the interviewee, whilst leaving them feeling good about themselves at the end of the experience where possible.

The start of the interview
In order for an interviewee to open up to you in the interview, they need to feel comfortable.
They also need to believe that you, the interviewer, have an open and unbiased mind and that you are interested in them as a person. To share a little about you can assist in helping the interviewee to relax.

It is also important that the interviewee knows that you have all the relevant records in the interview room and they can refer to them at any stage of the interview. It can be useful for the interviewee to talk the interviewer though the records they made.

Finally the interviewee should be reassured that if he/she needs to take a break then this is quite OK.

Explaining the purpose of the interview
Once the interviewee is seated and the preliminary introductions are complete, it is important to explain the purpose of the interview and the role of the interviewer and interviewee in this. The important points to get across are:

- That the primary purpose of the investigation is to find out as much as possible about the incident from everyone involved.
- To understand how the incident occurred.
- That the interviewer "wasn't there" so the interviewee needs to tell him/her everything he/she can remember, no matter how trivial the interviewee thinks it is.

[21] The content of this appendix is based on information gathered from Milne R and Bull R (2000) *Investigative Interviewing, Psychology and Practice*, Wiley and Sons

The interviewee's story/account

In this phase, the interviewee describes the incident from their perspective. It is important that the interviewee is not interrupted at any stage of their account. To interrupt the interviewee is to upset the memory retrieval process they are going through and to condition them to the expectation of being interrupted. This will only result in the interviewee being selective with the information shared, and tailoring their recount to fit in with the interviewer's interruptions. For the interviewer, body language is also important. The way you sit, inclines your head, or murmur the occasional encouraging noise, may affect the ease with which the interviewee recounts their experience, or the perception the interviewee has of your level of interest in what he/she has to tell you.

It can be a real test of your skill and patience not to interrupt an interviewee when they are telling their story, or recounting their contacts and involvement with a patient/client/service user. It is something that gets easier with practice.

Asking questions

When the interviewee has completed their story, the interviewer may then ask questions for either clarification purposes, or to try and draw more information from the interviewee.
It is normally recommended that the questions asked should only be related to what the interviewee has told you, and not related to what someone else has told you. However, in the health and social care scenario, this is often not practical. Frequently the interviewer will be aware of the broad sequence of events associated with an incident and they will need to ask the interviewee relevant questions even if they have not volunteered the information. It is the experience of many healthcare managers that interviewees are often reluctant to divulge crucial details because they don't want to be seen as a whistle blower. Generally speaking, it is the experience of the author that with encouragement interviewees will speak quite freely about their own actions and why they took these.

If the interviewer has to explore areas about which the interviewee has not made reference, it is essential that the interviewer respect the honesty of the interviewee if he/she tells you that they do not know the answer to your question. It is often tempting to persist with a particular line of questioning because you believe that the interviewee must know something and is choosing not to divulge the information. To pester the interviewee may result in their alienation from the learning process. It is a matter of fact that memory fails over time. If the information the interviewer wants to elicit was not significant to the interviewee at the time, it should be unsurprising if memory recall is low.

Key pointers for successful questions are:

- Where possible, ask your questions in the same order that the interviewee has remembered the incident, or their care contacts.
- Complete all questions regarding each part of the chronology, before moving onto the next as far as is possible. This saves the interviewee having to jump around their memory bank. For example if you are asking questions about an assessment process then explore this area thoroughly before moving forward.
- Use open questions rather than closed questions. Use phrases such as "Tell me", "Describe to me" or "Walk me through your usual approach to....." or "Walk me through the process of ......".
- Use closed questions to clarify specific facts, or where you want to limit the interviewee's response. "What time did x happen? ", "Who was in the room with you?"

If you want to maximise the opportunity for memory recall, you might want to repeat back to the interviewee what they have told you before moving in to the questioning phase. This enables the interviewee to tell you if you have not heard everything correctly, it also may trigger further memory recall. This technique is also essential if you want to test out with the interviewee that you have understood them correctly. It is called "reflect back".

Note: Pre-designed questions do have a place in the investigative interview but they need to be used with care and only after the interviewee has told you all they can recall without interruption. Hopefully many of your questions will be answered during the free recall and clarification period without you needing to ask them.

If interview questions are agreed amongst an investigation team it is sensible to group and theme these. A simple process should be sufficient:

- Group all the case/care specific questions together. That is all the questions only persons involved in the case/care management can respond to.
- Group all systems based questions together and subdivide in to sensible groupings for example:

- questions about team working;
- questions about training;
- questions about clinical and management supervision; and
- specific questions about core policies and procedures (there may be an overlap with case specific questions here – be alert to this).

Order of questions

Decide as a team whether you are going to start with the interviewee telling you about the patient/client/service user etc, and then moving to case specific questions followed by systems based questions.

It is the experience of the author that interviewees generally prefer to get all questions to do with them and their personal contact with the patient/service user/client out of the way first and then move on to more general questions about the systems and processes of work.

Summary

Once the interviewer has finished asking questions, it is important that a summary of information shared is repeated back to the interviewee at each core stage of the interview. The rule here is to use the interviewee's language not yours (it is their testimony not yours).
This phase allows the interviewee to identify inaccuracies in what the interviewer has picked up and correct them. It also presents the final opportunity for obtaining new information, if there is any more to be had.

Closure

The closing of the interview is as important as the opening. It is during this phase that the interviewer must ensure that the interviewee is left in a positive frame of mind, if at all possible.

To assist this the interviewer should:

- return to neutral topics of conversation;
- thank the interviewee for attending and for providing the information they have;
- ask the interviewee if they have any questions they would like to ask;
- provide the interviewee with a contact name and number if they feel they need to talk about the event again, or need support in coming to terms with it; and
- double check any demographic details associated with the interviewee, e.g., place of work, etc.

Alert points for the interviewer

There are a number of issues of which interviewers must be aware if they are to be successful in their role.

Interviewers:

- like all people, suffer from concentration lapses;
- are as vulnerable to failures of memory recall as the interviewee. Similarly, their mind map of the world may result in them only storing the information they perceive to be of importance, rather than what is really important;
- when providing the interviewee with a statement to sign, following the interview, need to be aware that that research has shown such statements to be incomplete and not infrequently incorrect. The interviewee must have control of the content of the statement. The best way of assuring accuracy is to provide a full transcript of the interview. This is best achieved by digital recording. However transcribing interviews is very expensive. At the time of print independent investigators pay up to £135 per hour of recorded data for typed transcripts. It may be more pragmatic to provide the interviewee with a copy of the digital recording and good quality typed notes of the interview;
- need to be alert to any tendency to bring the interview to a close before the interviewee has shared all the information they had wanted to with the investigation team. The information exchange process is as much to do with the interviewee sharing with us what he/she believes is important and necessary, as it is about the interviewer's questions;
- need to be aware of any tendency to lead the interviewee in their responses to questions;
- need to be aware of the risks of "confirmation bias", that is, listening to information that confirms an interviewer's pre-conceived views, with a greater degree of attentiveness than other information provided during the interview. At its most harmful level, confirmation bias results in the screening out of information that does not confirm preconceived opinions and beliefs;
- must ensure that sufficient time is made available for the interview;
- must ensure that there is someone present specifically to take notes of the interview. This person must have the competencies to make a full record of the interview and not merely key words and phrases.

Appendix 4:

The round-the-table or team-based critical incident review

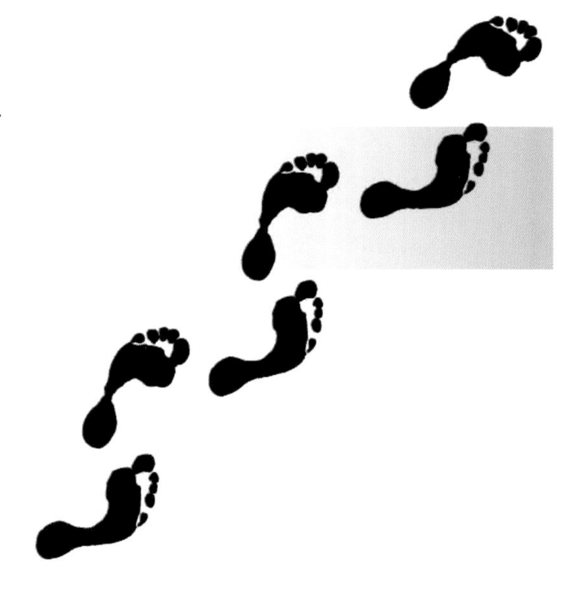

Introduction

The main content of this book has focused on an investigation process where it is the intention of the investigators to conduct individual interviews with staff. However, it is often possible to take a more dynamic approach to the investigation and explore what happened and why on a team basis by conducting the investigation along the same lines as a critical incident meeting, or a round-the table discussion. Opting for this approach has many merits but it is not without its challenges and pitfalls. The benefits are:

- staff feel safer. There is after all safety in numbers;
- it enables a proportional approach to be taken to less complex incidents; and
- it can be more time efficient.

The challenges/pitfalls are:

- there is a risk the investigation team will only hear the perspective of the more vocal persons present;
- getting those present to focus on the important issues of interest to the investigation team;
- exploring individual decisions about case management; and
- exploring communication pathways.

These challenges are not insurmountable. The investigators can:

- conduct a small number of one-to-one interviews if necessary;
- utilise the technique of "brain writing" to:
  - seek the individual perspectives of all present in relation to specific issues,
  - explore potentially sensitive issues for the team, where it could be predicted that some of the persons present may not openly contribute if they were required to verbalise their thoughts.

Practicalities that will aid the smooth running of a group critical incident review are, to ensure:

- that the investigator facilitates the meeting supported by at least one clinical advisor who is unrelated to the team involved where possible;
- you have a sufficiently large, light and airy room;
- that some refreshments are available;
- all relevant team members and other stakeholders are invited;
- the full timeline/simple chronology of the incident is either displayed, or provided to attendees via a handout;
- that you explain the investigative steps have undertaken at the start of the meeting;
- that there is opportunity provided for those present to read, and if appropriate challenge and/or add to your chronology at the start of the meeting; or
- that you allow time for participants to walk by and read the timeline if you have displayed this on a wall.

In addition to the above, if the case was particularly upsetting for staff, you may wish to consider some of the following:

- display the chronology in such a way that each section of time has a coded reference;
- ensure that there are a number of tamper proof boxes in the room (e.g. a "letter" box with a sealed lid and a slot);
- make available response proformas so that staff can comment privately on the content of the timeline, cross referencing their comments/observations to the coded reference assigned by the investigation team to the relevant time period; and
- posing core questions on a flip chart with a unique identifier for each and allowing participants to write down their responses and post in the tamper proof box. Staff can be provided with confidentiality, and anonymity, but it is helpful if staff are prepared to either provide their name or at the very least their job title, and relationship to the service user whose care is the subject of the investigation.

An alternative where more than one team or service is involved
An alternative to the round-the-table discussion where multiple teams are involved is the facilitated case presentation.

The facilitated case presentation follows a chaired meeting format. The principles are as detailed below:

- The meeting is opened by the chairperson who explains the purpose of the meeting and why all key involved teams have been invited.
- A set of ground rules are agreed by all. These might include:
  - that when one team is presenting, there are no interruptions;
  - that all in attendance treat each other with respect;
  - that attendees will not interrupt the team presenting their chronology of involvement with the patient/service user or client;
  - attendees will not ask questions of a team until invited to do so by the chairperson;
  - that questions as far as possible are asked in an open non-judgmental manner;
  - that what is spoken of in the room stays in the room; and
  - that all questions are directed at the chairperson to keep the meeting as non-personal as possible.
- The chair person asks each team in chronological order to present their involvement with the patient/service user/client.
- At the end of a team's presentation, the chairperson asks what with the benefit of hindsight should or could they have done differently (if anything).
- If an "independent" specialist advisor, or specialist advisors, are present the chairperson should ask these individuals for their observations, and for any questions for clarity to be posed to the teams/services present before opening the forum for a general discussion of the case management.
- The chairperson must ensure that all teams have completed their presentation before opening the meeting for general questions. This ensures that the case presentations can be completed in a timely way and minimises the risk of side tracking and unnecessary distraction during the first part of the meeting.

Bibliography

Anderson, B and Fagerhaug, T (2000) *Root cause analysis, simplified tools and Techniques.* ASQ Quality Press, Wisconsin, USA.

Gano, D L (1999) *Apollo root cause analysis, effective solutions to everyday problems every time*. Apollonian publications, Washington, USA.

HSE Books (1999) *Reducing error and influencing behaviour.* HSG 48.

HSE Books (2000) *Successful health and safety management.* HSG 65, second edition.

Latino, R and Latino, K (1999) *Root cause analysis, improving performance for bottom line results*. CRC Press, Florida, USA.

Milne, R and Bull, R (2000) *Investigative interviewing, psychology and practice*. Wiley and Sons.

Joint Commission on Accreditation of Healthcare Organizations (2000) *Root cause analysis in healthcare, tools and techniques.* JCAHO, Illinois, USA.

WS Atkins Consultants Ltd (2001) *Root cause analysis: literature review*. HSE Contract Research Report 325/2001.

Useful websites

Australian Patient Safety Foundation: www.apsf.net.au
Clinical Risk Unit, University College London: www.patientsafety.ucl.ac.uk
Consequence: www.consequence.org.uk
Joint Commission on Accreditation of Health Care Organizations: www.jcaho.org
National Patient Safety Agency: www.npsa.nhs.uk
Veterans Affairs National Centre for Patient Safety:
www.patientsafety.gov

World Health Organization – Patient Safety Portal: http://www.who.int/patientsafety/en/